# RABIES —
# YOU AND YOUR PETS

To my wife Joy whose forbearance made the task of writing this book a pleasant one, and to my typist Edith Baird for deciphering my scrawling and much amended draft with such commendable efficiency.

# RABIES–

## YOU AND YOUR PETS

ROY GIBBS

Melksham
COLIN VENTON
WHITE HORSE LIBRARY

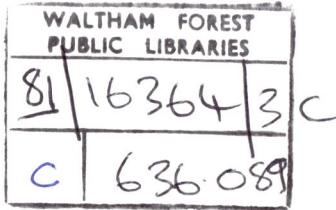

*Set 11 on 13 point Times Roman*
*And printed and bound in Great Britain,*
*At the Press of the Publisher,*
*The Uffington Press, High Street,*
*Melksham, Wiltshire, U.K.*

# LIST OF CONTENTS

# LIST OF ILLUSTRATIONS

List of Illustrations
(Continued)

# INTRODUCTION

Rabies, one of the oldest diseases known to man and from which there is only one recorded case of recovery, derives from the Sanskrit word "rhabas" — meaning to do violence. Caused by a bullet shaped virus, it attacks the nervous system and is carried in the saliva of the person or animal affected.

The disease which is constantly in existence among dogs and wolves in some countries, spreads wildly in epidemics. It also occurs commonly in foxes, coyotes and skunks as well as vampire bats. All warm blooded mammals are susceptible to the virus which has proved an economic problem in South America where thousands of cattle have succumbed to attacks from rabid vampire bats.

Rabies is most frequently acquired from a bite and the nearer the site of the wound to the brain, the shorter the incubation period and the greater chance of a quick death. Not all rabid animals harbour the virus in their saliva and there is more chance of escape if the bite is through clothing. The disease can also be transmitted through mucous membranes and, very rarely, by infection from droplets in the air containing the virus.

Victims of rabies become fevered and sick and develop a sense of apprehension. There is a terror of fluids caused by spasms of the swallowing muscles when trying to drink —hence the ancient name for the disease — hydrophobia. Bouts of wild destructive behaviour often follow. Death usually occurs within 6 days of the onset of symptoms and is preceded by convulsions and delirium.

## Rabies—You and Your Pets

Thanks to our quarantine laws, rabies has been practically non-existent in the U.K. since 1897. The last case of human infection contracted in Britain was in 1911. Since 1946, 11 cases have been diagnosed in this country all of which were acquired while the victims were overseas.

Cases of rabies in dogs in the U.K. in recent years have served to remind us that increasing vigilance is necessary if we are to remain protected from the ravages of the dread disease. Particularly is such vigilance necessary in view of the way rabies in animals is now spreading across Europe. Thus in France, for example, in 1973 there were 5,000 cases in animals recorded. In the whole of Western Europe only Denmark and Great Britain are now free of rabies.

Accordingly restrictions have been tightened up and under the Rabies Act, 1974, which came into force in February, 1975, all mammals except for farm livestock brought into this country must come through designated ports and airports, have an import licence and undergo a six month quaranteen period. Any animal brought in illegally may be destroyed on the spot and the offender fined an unlimited amount, sentenced to a year's imprisonment or both.

It also empowers the Government, in the event of the disease being confirmed in Britain again, to destroy foxes, ban hunts and dog and cat shows and destroy stray animals.

With the chances of rabies reappearing in Britain increasing year by year as it spreads across France, interest in the disease and its consequences has been re-awakened. This book is intended to be of general interest and in particular should be read by those whose jobs might bring them into contact with a rabid animal. It will also be useful reading for pet owners, animal lovers, owners of small boats and yacht marinas and all who travel to foreign parts. The information could, with value, be imparted to children in schools so that they are made aware in their formative years of what life would be like here should rabies become established.

*Chapter One*

# RABIES AND MAN

The disease, modes of infection and symptons — history worldwide — history in
Britain — recent cases in Britain — incidence of human deaths — a case of recovery

*THE DISEASE, MODES OF INFECTION AND SYMPTOMS*

Rabies, one of the oldest diseases known to man, almost certainly ends in death for the person unfortunate enough to contract it. Caused by a bullet shaped virus, it attacks the nervous system and is carried in the saliva of a rabid animal.

Transmission of the disease can occur from a bite, through a cut or other wound, via the mucous membrane or, exceptionally, by aerosol transmission. The most common route of transference is from a bite, when the saliva containing the virus infects the wound. The latter invades the nervous system and reaches the brain via the spine. The nearer the bite occurs to the brain, the shorter will be the incubation period and the greater chance of death being swift. The saliva of some rabid animals does not harbour the virus and there is a better chance of escaping rabies if a bite occurs through thick clothing. The virus can enter the system through the mucous membranes even if they are unbroken and cases of people developing the disease after eating the meat of rabid animals have been recorded.

Two Americans who died from laboratory confirmed rabies without being bitten by an infected animal were found to have visited a cave in Texas that was infected with rabid insectivorous bats. It was considered they had contracted the disease through breathing in droplets from the air. The incubation period of rabies in man varies

*11*

widely from as little as ten days to as long as two years depending on the severity of the bite, the distance from the brain and whether or not the area affected had any protection.

Typical symptoms of rabies include fever, headache and sickness with a sense of apprehension and a burning feeling at the spot where the bite occured. There will be spasms of the swallowing muscles when trying to drink. These terrify the patient and lead to a fear of fluids—a sympton that gave rise to the ancient name for the disease—hydrophobia. There may be an aversion to bright light and although mental faculties may largely be maintained, there may be bouts of wild destructive behaviour. Convulsions and delirium often follow and death usually occurs two to six days from the onset of the symptoms.

## HISTORY — WORLDWIDE

The first mention of rabies in history dates back to 2300 B.C. when the ancient Babylonians decreed by law that an owner, when informed by the local authority that his dog was mad, had to keep it confined. If he failed in his duty and it bit someone he was forced to pay a specified fine which varied according to whether he was a freeman or a slave.

Until Aristotle, in 322 B.C., established the connection between the disease in animals and man, it was believed that wildness in animals was caused by evil spirits. A well known physician of the first century A.D., Celsus, recognized that the saliva of a rabid animal was venomous and was the means of passing on the disease. He recommended treating a bite with sea water. A later physician advocated hurling the unfortunate victim into a pond!

In Europe the pattern of the disease in previous centuries was outbreaks in domestic and wild dogs followed by secondary infections of other animals over a wide area and some humans. It is now thought that these outbreaks may have been attributable to infection among foxes. There are many stories of people being attacked in the early part of the 19th century by rabid foxes in Saxony, Bavaria, Southern Germany, Austria, Switzerland, Holland and Sweden.

In 1885 Louis Pasteur who, with his colleagues, had been researching deeply into rabies, successfully vaccinated a boy who had been bitten by a rabid dog. Pasteur knew that the disease was caused by a minute organism which, in 1962 was described by Mastsumoto, a Japanese doctor, as being bullet shaped. Earlier, in 1936, its size had been established by filtration as being 0.0018mm long and 0.000075mm in diameter.

## HISTORY IN BRITAIN

Until the end of the 19th century rabies had been present in Britain for the greater part of the time that her history had been recorded. In 1831, the first attempt to control the spread of 'canine madness', took the form of a Bill which never became law, but which was tabled as a result of a serious problem in the Midland Urban areas. Later, local authorities were given powers to require muzzling, to restrict dog's movements and to destroy strays. Between 1886 and 1903 there were 173 human deaths from rabies in England and Wales. The powers given to local authorities were not effectually used and were taken over by the Board of Agriculture.

In 1897 an order was introduced that prohibited the landing of dogs except with a licence from the Board. Dogs had to be detained for six months on their owner's premises and muzzled when exercised. The regulations were evaded and in 1901 amended so that dogs had to be detained and isolated under a veterinary surgeon's supervision for six months.

Within a year Britain was free of rabies and remained so until 1918 when a rabid dog smuggled in at Plymouth caused 129 cases. It took a further four years to bring the disease under control once again. During that period 144 people who had been bitten by suspected dogs had to undergo the painful and prolonged course of vaccinations. The real risk to which they had been exposed was borne out by the fact that 123 of the dogs concerned were found, during laboratory test, to have been affected by the rabies virus.

## RECENT CASES IN BRITAIN

Between 1946 and 1971 eight cases of rabies were confirmed in Britain in humans. In each case the infection was acquired abroad. The increasing use and speed of air travel and the rising numbers of commonwealth immigrants who return after visiting their homelands for holidays, inevitably mean the increased chances of the odd case developing here after contraction of the virus abroad.

Three such cases occurred in 1975 and 1976 and reports by hospital staff serve to graphically illustrate the horrors of the disease for the patients and those attending them medically. A 37-year old New Zealander, Val Ingham, who was bitten on the lip by a rabid puppy in Gambia, West Africa during the summer of 1975 died a month after being admitted to the National Hospital for Nervous Diseases in London. Before being transferred to London, Mr. Ingham was taken to a Gambian hospital where a nurse reported that he jumped out of bed screaming and ran towards a window when offered a glass of water, shouting ''Don't bring that towards me''. In London he continually had spasms and hysterically spat out his saliva because he was terrified of drowning in it. Earlier the same month a 22 year old student, Robert Apps, died in University College Hospital London, a month after returning from India where he had been bitten by a rabid dog.

In June 1976 a 52 year old restaurant kitchen assistant, Mohammed . Muslim, of Bangladesh origin, died from rabies in a Manchester hospital. Admitted with stomach pains, he was operated on for appendicitis, but unknown to the hospital staff, he had been bitten by a dog during a

*14*

visit to his native Bangladesh. Relatives, questioned as to the date of the incident, were vague and gave various possible dates—the most likely of which seemed to be in April 1975. After the operation he started mumbling loudly and then became hysterical . . . He was given a sedative which had no effect and his body began to twist about and his legs to thrash the air. Exhibiting the classic symptoms of rabies he was moved to a side room where he died shortly afterwards. During the last stages of the illness, a doctor knowing that saliva could transmit the disease, thrust a tube down the patient's throat to assist him breathing in his agony. A colleague doubted whether he should have done this but described it as a most heroic action.

Before he was moved to the side ward the patient, thrashing about in agony bit a nurse, Margaret Kernaghan, on the hand. Although realising that saliva entering a break in the skin can pass rabies, the 19 year old girl continued to ease Mr. Muslim's distress. The following day she started a daily series of the duck egg embryo vaccination in the stomach wall. Three days later she was too ill to attend lectures, but told how, after a routine operation, the patient began growling and howling, disturbing the whole hospital. Drugs had no effect and he suffered convulsions and was violently sick. Saliva began foaming from his mouth and he was unable to control his movements. He tried to hurl himself from the bed and before she could catch him and stop his head hitting the floor, he bit her. It was not a deep bite but it was accompanied by saliva. By then six members of the staff were trying to restrain him and he appeared to be asking for water. When offered a glass he spat the water out and went mad. The doctor then warned the nurse that it looked like rabies—a disease she had never studied and didn't expect to meet. Even though she remembered what she'd seen in television documentaries about rabies, she carried on with her duties all the time knowing there

was little anyone could do to save him.

She stayed on after she should have come off duty. Suddenly the patient died and she left for the nurse's home feeling shaky and low. The next day Margaret began the course of injections which made her feel continually sick. She knew they were only given as a precaution — but she also knew that rabies could take more than a year to develop and the possibility would be at the back of her mind for many months.

So seriously do the authorities now view the dangers from rabies that it was not surprising that Manchester's city coroner only released Mohammed Muslim's body for burial in Bangladesh, with the greatest regret and because he had no powers to refuse it. The medical authorities in the area denied there was a risk saying "rabies dies with the victim". The virus is not very stable and a rabies expert in London said there was little risk, even to the relatives who washed the body according to the ritual of the deceased's religion. The Coroner said the body, having been washed several times in a suitable agent, was lying in linen sheets soaked in the agent and contained in two separate polythene bags. He had the authority of the hospital to release it but it was a very grave source of infection — a statement no doubt prompted by the massive rabies publicity campaign mounted by the Government coincidentally at the same time as the case in point.

An 11 year old Pakistani boy died of rabies in Bradford Royal Infirmary in March 1977 ten weeks after having been bitten by a rabid dog in his grandparents' village in Pakistan. The boy went for a check up following the bite but all seemed well. He had lived with his grandparents for four years and told no one of the incident on his return to England on February 13th. After falling down-stairs at his Bradford home he was taken to hospital for an X-Ray but allowed home after bruising on the left thigh had been examined. 48 hours later he began exhibiting the classic symtoms of rabies and died 20 minutes after admission to hospital.

Prior to being X-Rayed the boy had fallen twice and hurt himself and complained of being thirsty. The night after the X-Ray visit, his body began convulsing and he was foaming at the mouth. The medical authorities said had they known about the biting incident the day he returned from Pakistan, the chances of saving his life would have been remote.

Later the boys' parents were, unlike the case previosly described, refused permission to fly the body to Pakistan for burial because of the risk of infection. A plan to hold a funeral service at a local mosque was refused for the same reason. A service was held at the local mortuary where only close relatives, who had previously been vaccinated against rabies, were allowed to be present. After the body had been double wrapped in polythene, it was buried in a specially sealed casket.

## INCIDENCE OF HUMAN DEATHS

According to Dr. G. S. Turner, a virologist with the Lister Institute of Preventive Medicine, man has a low susceptibility to the rabies virus and deaths from the disease are rare. No one has died from rabies in France since 1968 and in Germany only one death was recorded from the disease between 1966 and 1973, although in 1974 there were three. Slightly higher figures are reported from Poland, Yugoslavia and Rumania. As one would expect, in less developed countries the figures are greater, e.g. in Pakistan, Bangladesh and Latin America. When compared, however, with deaths from malnutrition and malaria, the number of people succumbing to rabies in these countries is relatively small.

Dr. Turner considers that in the West some 15% of people bitten by rabid dogs would die without treatment. Prompt treatment would reduce this figure to 1%.

2

## A CASE OF RECOVERY

The only recorded case of a human surviving rabies was six year old Matt Winkler who lived in the American State of Ohio near the town of Rockford. One night in October 1970, together with his four year old sister Valerie, he lay sleeping in their room upstairs. At ten o'clock came screams from the bedroom. Matt's mother, Verna Winkler, dashed upstairs and saw a furry object clinging to his thumb. She called her husband Nick who burst into the room and pulled a brown bat from his son's hand. Verna quickly washed the bite marks on Matt's thumb and soaked them with alcohol. Because he knew bats could harbour rabies Nick decided to keep the bat; he placed it in a jar and took it next day to a vet, who sent it to a laboratory in Columbus.

Matt was taken to his doctor who decided to wait until he knew whether or not the bat was rabid, before embarking on the painful series of 14 daily vaccinations. The laboratory reported within a few days that rabies had been isolated from the bat's brain. Matt then started the treatment; but many Americans had been similarly dealt with and all but two had escaped rabies that year — there was little cause for concern at that stage.

Towards the end of the month the boy became unwell and antibiotics were given after a diagnosis of suspected 'flu. Four days later Matt's temperature rose sharply and his neck became stiff. The doctor sought the advice of a colleague w..o agreed the boy might be reacting to the vaccine — a phenomenon that does occur in some people. He was moved to a hospital in Lima where again it was thought he might be suffering from 'flu. The doctor who examined him had a lingering doubt because on the records he wrote "Although no rabies, suggest avoid rare possibility of child's bite". What were the chances of Matt having rabies? Each year some 100,000 Americans are bitten by animals and about 20,000 have the course of injections.

Between 1950 and 1969 only 138 people, both treated and untreated, have contracted rabies — but they all died — since medical history began rabies has been the only irreversible disease.

Matt appeared to progress and a month after he had been bitten was nearly ready to be sent home. He frequently went to sleep but this was put down to boredom. Soon after the periods of sleep increased and he again had a stiff neck. A spinal fluid test revealed white blood cells — a sign of irritation of the nervous system. Vaccine reaction rarely caused so long an illness but Matt might have caught another form of virus. There was still no symptoms of rabies. Suddenly Matt's speech became confused and soon he was unable to speak. Then the very real possibility of rabies became apparent and was subsequently proved by blood tests.

After the boy had lapsed into semi-consciousness a doctor, expert in rabies, was called. Dr. Michael Hattwick was one of the few medicos who believed that the disease could be treated. He told Verna that her son had every chance of survival. In his studies of rabies cases Dr. Hattwick had noticed that death came when breathing stopped. Other complications became apparant almost - simultaneously. He drew up a list of signs they could expect to see and how they would deal with them. After moving him into a private room they taped electrodes to his chest to monitor his heart. Together with the resident doctor he double checked the boy's condition. Matt remained deceptively calm as they waited for a crisis. One night as they were making a final check they noticed his heart beat and breathing had accelerated although he was sleeping. The pale face and blue lips were signs of air starvation that had ended in death in many other cases.

The doctors realized that Matt needed an artificial aid to help him to breathe. They warned Nick and Verna that an operation to insert an air-way into the boy's throat would be hazardous because of his weakened condition. The parents consented and the operation was a success. The doctors waited for other signs of the disease. Matt could not talk and was partially paralysed down the left side—the side on which the bat had bitten him and he could not feed himself or co-ordinate movement.

A random clutching in the left hand might have been the beginning of convulsions. The movement ceased after the boy had received anticonvulsant drugs three times a day. Shortly after, his condition became stable. Slowly speech and power of movement returned and, three months after admission to hospital, he was ready to go home — on his seventh birthday.

*Footnote*

Two cases of recovery from rabies, not given publicity at the time were reported in the Editorial of the British Medical Journal in 1975. The patients received intensive care enabling them to survive crises at various stages of the illness.

The first fatal human case of rabies that has occurred in Switzerland for some thirty years, involved a thirty five year old man who lived in the Aargau Canton. Bitten by a dog and a cat during 1976, he developed the disease and died the following February in a hospital at Baden.

# RABIES

La rage tue. Obeyez les lois de quarantaine.

Die Tollwut tötet. Folgt den Quarantänegesetzen.

La rabia mata. Obedecen Vds. los leyes de cuarentena.

L'idrofobia uccide. Ubbidete le legge di quarantena.

Rabies kills. Obey the quarantine laws.

Mondsdolheid doodt. Gehoorzaamt de quarantainewetten.

# Kills in any language

Rabies is a killer disease of humans and animals. This country is free of rabies and our quarantine laws are designed to keep it so. You can help by ensuring that any animal entering this country has the necessary documents which are obtainable from the local office of the Ministry of Agriculture.

East Sussex County Council

*Figure* 1—Rabies Kills in any language. (Leaflet).

# To travel your pet needs a passport

It is illegal to bring an animal into this country (even if its home is here) without the necessary documents. If you intend holidaying abroad with your pet or you want to bring a pet home from abroad, consult the local office of the Ministry of Agriculture.

## *Rabies Kills!*

East Sussex County Council

*Figure* 2—To travel your pet needs a passport. (Leaflet).

Chapter Two

## RABIES AND PETS

Symptoms of the disease — incubation periods —species affected — history in Britain — incidence abroad.

### *SYMPTOMS OF THE DISEASE*

Should a rabid dog or cat be illegally imported into Britain and, after developing symptons, attack other pets in the area or a similar incident arise after an animal has been released from quarantine, owners would want to know what to look for in their own animals.

A dog can exhibit rabies in three phases :—

(1) a dumb or melancholy stage

(2) a furious stage, and

(3) a paralytic stage

It has been shown that the furious stage is encountered in only about 25 per cent of cases.

In the dumb rabies stage, which usually lasts some three days, the dog's temperament will be the opposite to normal; a quiet and shy dog will become aggresive and noisy while a usually excitable dog will appear dull and quiet. This could be a dangerous stage because the symptoms could easily be mistaken for other conditions, no thought being given to the possibility of rabies, a disease that very few people have seen.

The furious stage of rabies would be more likely to alert the owner and others meeting the dog, to the chances that it was rabid. The dog will tend to run away from its home and travel 30 or 40 miles snapping and biting at anything or anyone it meets. It will appear unbalanced and act ferociously. It may have intervals of normality and return

*21*

home without arousing suspicion. At this stage it may eat and drink quickly or alternatively be off its food. It commonly eats stones, pieces of wood or coal and will, understandably, be inclined to vomit.

The paralytic stage will follow in a few days. The lower jaw drops, leaving the tongue hanging out and saliva dripping. Staggering, due to paralysis of the back legs, will be seen. The dog will eventually collapse and after a series of convulsions death will follow within 3 or 4 days. Contrary to what is popularly believed a rabid dog has no fear of water and will try to drink even when swallowing becomes impossible. The term hydrophobia is thus misleading if applied to rabies in dogs.

Symptoms seen in rabid dogs may occur and be due to other causes. Production of excessive saliva can accompany epileptic fits and convulsions could follow poisoning or brain damage sustained through being hit by a motor vehicle. A combination of aggressiveness, frothing at the mouth, a reeling gait and convulsions sometimes follow a bout of canine distemper.

In cats, the furious stage of the disease is more commonly seen than in dogs and can be particularly dangerous as scratching and biting could both be involved, and because the change of temperament quite often takes the form of an increase in affection.

As with the dog, symptoms seen following poisoning, can be confused with those usually attributed to rabies.

## INCUBATION PERIODS

The incubation period of rabies in dogs and cats normally varies between two weeks and two months but as short a period as a week and as long a one as a year have been recorded. In quarantine in Britain some half of the cases occurred in less than a month from importation and 80 per cent within four months, but it is impossible to know when infection took place and the journey to this country may have taken several weeks. As the majority of dogs and cats are transported by air today it might appear that incubation periods are longer because arrival is more quickly after infection. In determining the period of quarantine in the U.K., it was borne in mind that in many foreign countries an animal known to have been bitten by a rabid animal is destroyed. It was assumed, therefore, that any imported animal found to be affected would have received a small rather than a large dose of virus. Consequently cases of rabies in quarantine would tend to have longer incubation periods.

Of the 27 cases of rabies that occurred in quarantine in Britain between 1924 and 1969, the periods between landing and death of the animal varies from 2 days to 7 months.

In the first case the dog's temperament changed during the voyage and in the second the dog was detained in isolation at the request of its owner after the quarantine period had expired. Of the 27 cases, 25 were in dogs, one in a cat and one in a leopard. 12 of the dogs were various breeds of terrier and importations from India accounted for 11.

Two cases of rabies in dogs have occurred in recent years outside quarantine. In 1969, Fritz — a German Schnauzer type dog — developed symptoms a week after release from quarantine (see Chapter 3) due to cross infection in the kennels, and the following year a terrier cross bitch brought from Pakistan first showed signs of the illness three months after being taken home from quarantine kennels in Newmarket.

## SPECIES AFFECTED

All warm blooded creatures can transmit rabies. Traditionally the dog has been thought of as the most common carrier and because of its close proximity to man is still the most likely animal to pass it on to him. This is particularly true of India where the disease is widespread and where in 1958 no fewer than 50,000 dogs were confined as rabid.

On a world basis, data published by the World Health Organisation in 1973 showed that dogs have only a moderate susceptibility to rabies while cats have a high one. Also appearing on the "high susceptibility" list are hamsters, guinea pigs, rabbits and other rodents — all likely pets of British youngsters.

Examples of humans being attacked by the smaller type of exotic pet are rare. A Peruvian ocelot, taken to the U.S.A. after vaccination by a government vet., died of the disease after attacking five people, and a pet skunk living in the same country succumbed to rabies after biting two of its owners while being bathed. In Canada a pet rabbit bit two children after contracting rabies while the most famous case in history concerned the Duke of Richmond, governor-general of that country at the time, who died after being bitten by a rabid fox in 1819.

## *HISTORY IN BRITAIN*

There were a number of outbreaks of rabies, mainly among dogs, in the eighteenth and nineteenth centuries. The first attempts to control the disease involved the destruction of stray dogs around rapidly growing urban areas. Some success was achieved in the London area but the lack of a co-ordinated national policy saw the problem worsening as the Twentieth century approached. In 1874 rabid animals caused the deaths of 74 persons although Norway and Sweden had, by that time, achieved eradication by regulating animal movements and eliminating strays.

Powers given to local authorities to enforce the muzzling of dogs in infected areas were unpopular with dog owners and were not enforced. Central government took over and the disease waned.

By 1892 anti muzzling feeling among the public led to enforcement being handed back to local authorities and the disease once more became prevalent. From 1889-1898 160 people died from rabies. In 1897 stronger national legislation was introduced and, five years later, rabies in the U.K. had been eradicated. The country has remained free apart from the period 1918-1922 when an outbreak occurred, due it was thought, to troops returning from the continent and illegally bringing their pets with them.

The publicity given to rabies has brought to light an interesting case history. A Sussex doctor discovered a press cutting of a letter sent in 1833 by a predecessor in his practice to his local newspaper. In that year a rabid dog had wandered from Lewes to Chailey biting others on the way. The doctor worried at the apparent ignorance of those handling rabid animals wrote that if the hands are not perfectly sound or there is the least abrasion of the skin, it should be remembered that the application of saliva to the flesh wound is often followed by rabies as from the bites of the rabid animal. The power of infection, he went on, exists in the virus at every period of the confirmed disease and for about 24 hours after death. Its vehicle is not only the saliva and the mucous of the mouth but also the blood, the substance of the salivary glands, and even the nerves themselves.

As proof that the disease may be communicated by saliva the doctor cited a case of a woman who owned a French poodle of which she was very fond and which was allowed to lick her face. She had a pimple on her chin from which she rubbed off the top and allowed the dog to induluge in its usual caresses, it licked the pimple of which the surface was exposed. She acquired hydrophobia and died.

Apart from cutting out the infection or amputating the limb, the doctor recommended that the instant a person had been bitten by a real or suspected rabid animal, he should resort to the nearest pump, stream or pool of water and continue to wash and sponge the part to remove all saliva from the wounds as well as from the surrounding parts

In the meantime hot water should be poured from a

considerable height on the wound until the nearest pract-
ioner arrives. By this means the poison is diluted and driven
out of the wound by the force employed. The doctor's
present day counterpart added in a footnote that the 1833
treatment for rabid bites cannot be improved upon.

At about the same time it was commonly believed that
rabies could arise spontaneously in a dog and only then
be passed on to another animal by a bite. This belief may
have accounted for the national opposition to muzzling
orders in force towards the end of the nineteenth century.

A certain Dr. Bardsley was well ahead of his time when in
1794, having noticed that a local pack of hounds had been
kept free from rabies by the Master quarantining every new
comer about to join the pack, advocated universal quarantine
for dogs within the kingdom and total prohibition of their
import. Fox hounds at this time were particularly vulnerable
as it was common for some to be lost during hunting and
to roam the countryside **before** returning home several days
later, with the consequent **risk of** attack from a rabid dog at
large.

*RABIES INCIDENCE ABROAD*

In Central and Southern America where rabies is commonly transmitted to cattle by bats, the disease in the dog is
rare. This could be because of its resistance to the bat type
virus or through an acquired immunity but by no means
ensures safety for an imported dog.

In 1968 domestic animals accounted for 20% of laboratory confirmed cases in the U.S.A. California reported more
cases than any other State, by far the biggest number
occurring in skunks which the U.S. Department of Health
advised should be quarantined for at least 3 months after
capture and vaccinated at least a month before release to an
owner.

The last thirty years has seen a dramatic increase in the
incidence of rabies in Canadian animals where the skunk,

next to the fox, is the most common carrier. Between 1925 and 1967, 19 human deaths were recorded in Canada.

Rabies has been active in Spain for at least a decade. In 1968 800,000 dogs were vaccinated against the disease and in 1975 when cases were reported from the Costa del Sol area, 9,000 stray dogs and cats were destroyed. Teams of inspectors patrolled the tourist coast armed with special rifles which fired anti-rabies pellets into animals they were unable to catch. One man died after being bitten by his own pet and failing to seek treatment. Pet owners all along the coast were ordered to muzzle their dogs and leash them when out in the streets. Failure to take these precautions meant an automatic £80 fine.

Similar action was taken in France in 1976 when the Government ordered all local authorities in the North and East to round up and kill stray cats on the spot in an attempt to halt the spread of rabies. Dogs were given a 48-hour stay of execution to allow their owners to claim them. The latter were then obliged to produce a certificate to prove their pet had been vaccinated against rabies.

On the continent cats are taking over from dogs in some countries as the chief transmitters of rabies. This has occured in Belgium, Denmark, Luxembourg and Switzerland. In the latter country during the years 1967-70, of 50 people needing treatment after animal attacks, 68 per cent were from cats compared with only 2 per cent from dogs.

Strict controls have kept Australia and New Zealand completely free from rabies. No dog may be landed in either of these countries from Asia, and New Zealand will only take in those born in Australia and Great Britain or those from the latter that have been out of quarantine for six months with no rabies in those particular kennels during the last three months and if they have been anti-rabies inoculated not more than 12 months nor less than 1 month prior to the date of export.

## CAT DEVELOPS RABIES SYMPTOMS

The coincidence of a cat, having been brought from France about a year previously and having gone wild, biting and scratching its owner, gave rise to the possibility that it might have rabies.

It was in April, 1978 that Peggity, a three legged cat who had served its time in quarantine, went berserk in its mistress's home at Heathfield and when seen by a local veterinary surgeon, was exhibiting the classic symptoms of the disease. The house was declared an 'infected place' and the cat rushed to high-security Ministry of Agriculture kennels at Wye in Kent where, after ten days of tests, it was decided that her symptoms were probably caused a form of chemical poisoning, possibly slug pellets.

Her owner's home was then released from quarantine and her other cat, Izzy, allowed out for the first time since the rabies scare began. Her owner had in the meantime undergone anti-rabies treatment.

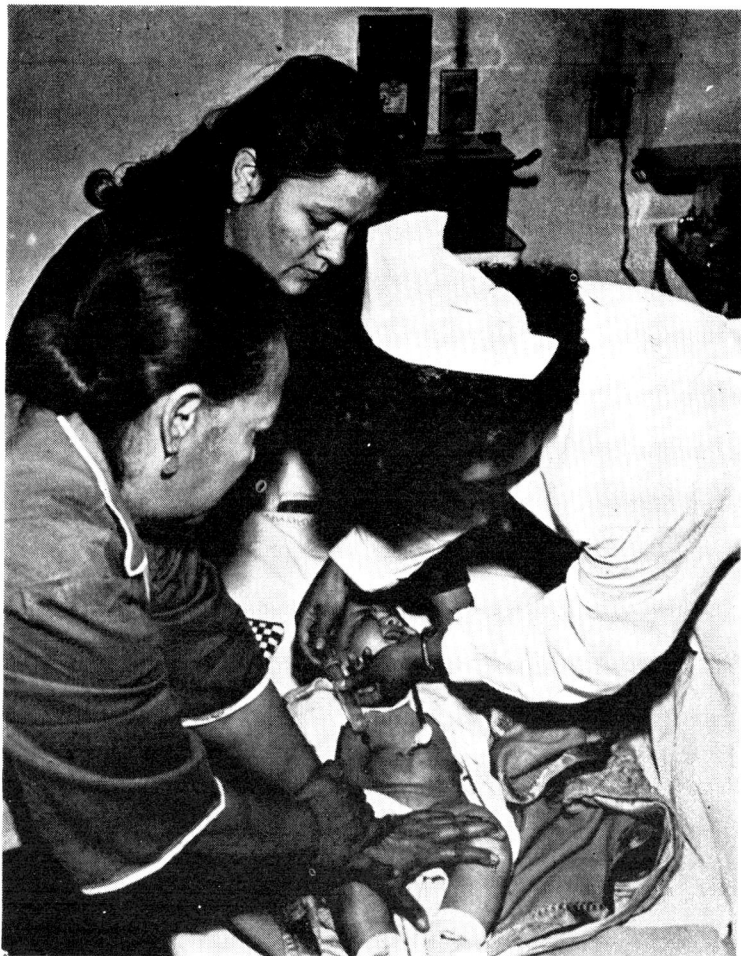

*Plate* 1—An anxious mother watches by her baby who is given an anti-rabies shot in the inoculation room of the anti-rabies centre in Mexico city. (*WHO photo*).

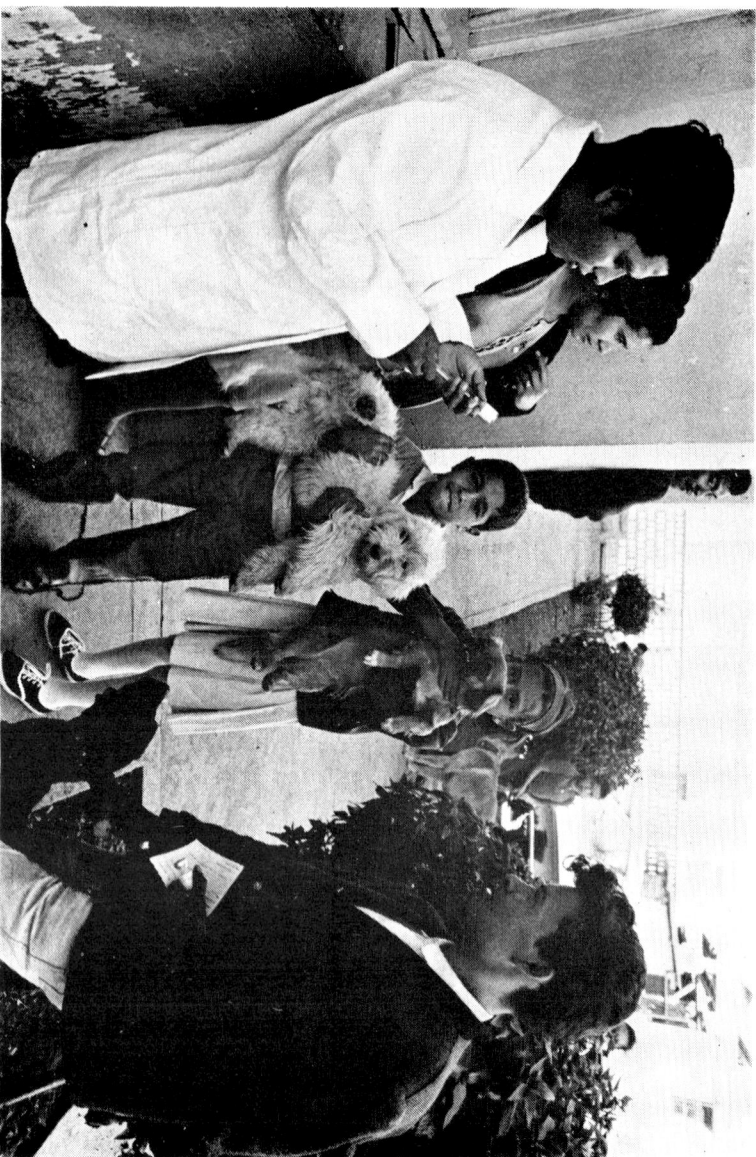

Plate 2—Guatemalan children waiting with their dogs at a public health office for free anti-rabies injections. (*WHO photo by P. Larsem*).

## Chapter Three

## RABIES AND THE CAMBERLEY INCIDENT

Background of dog — Fritz at large — Fritz in captivity with rabies — action after the incident — hunting — destruction of wild life — action by the medical authorities — stray dogs.

## BACKGROUND OF DOG

It had been 47 years since the last case of rabies occurred in an animal outside quarantine kennels in Britain when, in October 1969, a 2½- year old terrier type dog developed the furious type of the disease six days after release from quarantine. The dog, Fritz, resembled a schnauzer. Its father was unknown — its mother a Norwegian Buhund. Originating from Bielefield in Germany where its owners Major and Mrs Hemsley had been stationed, it had, while there, occasionally been exercised in near-by woods where buck, foxes and squirrels were to be found. As far as was known there had been no fighting or biting incidents involving the dog. In April 1969 Fritz was brought home to England by car on the Calais-Dover ferry. He was collected by an authorised carrier and taken direct to quarantine kennels. On completion of the six months quarantine period, on October 4th, he was collected by his owners and and taken home.

## FRITZ AT LARGE

Six days later on October 10th Fritz crawled under a bed and howled. His hind legs became stiff and a day later he refused food and water. The next day he ate a little food but refused to drink and preferred to stay under the bed. On October 13th he became excitable, snapping in an aggressive manner and barking in a strange voice. He was

*29*

let out into the garden early the following morning and appeared to be very constipated. It was then discovered that he had bitten through a milk-man's boot and killed a cat. Fritz then disappeared. His owners became alarmed and sought advice of a neighbour, an army veterinary surgeon, who said the dog should be recaptured immediately and locked up.

Some three quarters of an hour later Fritz was seen jumping into a taxi full of school children and by now appeared to be in a highly rabid condition. The owner managed to pull him out of the taxi and called for help. She tied a length of string around his muzzle but was bitten on the arm and leg in the process. Fritz was then locked in a ground floor lavatory.

## FRITZ IN CAPTIVITY WITH RABIES

After Fritz had been recaptured, details of the incident were passed from the army veterinary surgeon to the divisional veterinary officer who sent one of his officers to examine the dog and arrange for him to be removed to quarantine kennels. A licensed carrier agreed to stand by to move him. The medical officer of health and the police were told of the suspected disease. Fritz was examined, rabies was suspected and he was placed in a nose and paw proof crate, carried to the van under a veterinary officer's supervision and taken to the kennels. Here he was isolated in an empty block under special security guard. The whole crate was placed in the kennel and Fritz released by remote handling outside the cage.

Before the dog left for kennels, the local public health inspector was making enquiries to trace human contacts and veterinary officers were busy on similar work involving animal contacts and any biting or scratching incidents in which Fritz had been involved. The latter's owners were closely questioned and could state categorically that there was only one occasion — in January of that year in Germany

—when the dog had run off for about a quarter of an hour. Details of his recent movements were recalled. The owners of nine dogs with whom he had had contact were visited and served with notices requiring their dogs to be kept at home. They were all frequently examined and remained healthy.

Fritz was examined daily and showed classical symptoms of rabies — high pitched howling ended with a stifled yell — fixed, staring expression and abnormal strength apparent by his ability to move the heavy crate across the kennel. Two days later he lost co-ordination of his fore and hind legs and there was nervous twitching and spasmodic trembling. On the 17th he exhibited violent convulsions, bumping haphazardly around the kennel and biting his own legs. He finally collapsed and lay still and by 8.30 the following morning was dead.

The body was packed into plastic bags and delivered to the Central Veterinary Laboratory where the post mortem confirmed a positive rabies diagnosis. The report showed that the carcase was congested, the pancreas blood-spotted and there was acute gastritis. A hair bolus and blood clot were found in the duodenum and hair and broom bristles in the stomach. The spleen was congested and there were bites on the fore-legs.

## ACTION AFTER THE INCIDENT

Fritz's bedding, basket, feeding utensils and the lavatory where he was confined before removal to quarantine, were disinfected under the chief public health inspector's supervision. The veterinary officer took responsibility for similar work on the carrier's van, equipment and the kennel where he was isolated. All loose and combustible material, including the travelling crate, were taken to a small exercise yard and burned. The kennel was scrubbed with hot washing soda solution and again disinfected.

The house which was Fritz's home was in the middle of a housing estate with open-plan gardens at the front and bounded on the sides by two commons. Fritz had been known to play with other dogs on the estate although he was not given to roaming. He could have had access to the commons and was exercised regularly on one part of it by his owner.

Because Fritz had been free during his 45-minute period of madness the Ministry decided to place restrictions on all dogs living within a third of a mile of the dog's home. Dogs were confined to their houses and gardens and not allowed contact with other animals. Exercise in public places could only take place if the animals were leashed, muzzled and under effective control of their owners. Because it was considered impracticable and unnecessáry, domestic cats were not placed under similar restrictions.

The police logged all messages and enquiries about the incident and drew up a questionnaire to be completed by some three hundred householders who were required to state whether they owned a dog. If so, the breed, sex, age, colour and markings and name had to be given. Also required was a photograph of each dog to help the public identify those that had associated with Fritz. A total of 310 houses were visited and restriction notices served in 74 cases.

On October 24th a letter from the Ministry of Agriculture was delivered to 14,000 houses in the Camberley Urban district area describing rabies symptoms and asking for dog owners who had exercised their animals near Fritz's home or on the commons adjoining, between the 4th and 14th, to contact the nearest police station. The tremendous response to the letter by telephone and personal enquiry meant extra staff to give information and reassurance. As a result a further 85 modified restriction notices were served. Regular spot checks were made by police officers to see that notices were being observed. When owners went on holiday, moved house or left the area, the divisional veterinary officer in the area was notified and a new restriction notice served.

## HUNTING

As there was little chance that Fritz had been in contact with wild life it was thought important to disturb wild animals as little as possible. All hunting was voluntarily suspended within a ten mile radius of the restricted area. Three hunts had kennels situated within the area and packs had been hunted or exercised over the commons during the danger period. Confinement to kennels would have resulted in boredom with possible fighting and injury and the dogs would have been unfit to hunt during the 1970/1 season. The hounds were allowed to use restricted runs on two selected Army firing ranges where the public was excluded. Coupling of the dogs was left to the discretion of the person in charge but the pack had always to remain under effective control.

## DESTRUCTION OF WILD LIFE

Surveys carried out over the commons showed that foxes and squirrels were abundant but there were few badgers, rabbits or hares. Ministry veterinary officers had to decide on action to be taken to reduce the risk of rabies becoming endemic in wild life. It was finally agreed to hold a 2-day shoot on the 30th and 31st October to destroy all foxes, badgers, hares, rabbits, squirrels and vermin on the commons within a radius of a mile and a half of Fritz's home. The radius chosen was thought to be the natural range of the fox. The area covered some 2,000 acres of mostly open heath together with some densely wooded areas.

All known foxs' lairs and badgers' setts had, during the survey, been treated with cyanide powder which was left to vaporise into gas and the holes sealed. A meeting at the Infestation Control Centre on October 28th attended by the R.S.P.C.A., British Deer Society, County Naturalist Trusts, medical officer of health, chief public health inspector,

*33*

chief veterinary surgeon, Southern Command and the police, unanimously supported the shoots. The 48-hours delay before shooting began enabled the police to seal off the commons and warn the public. Police warnings were relayed to local cinemas, schools, and public houses and warnings by loud speakers given to residents of a large council house estate adjoining the common with a special request that pets should be kept indoors.

The guns for the shoot were provided by Ministry establishments and the beaters came from a nearby Army camp. In all seven sweeps were made. Police officers with walkie-talkie pack sets were posted on each flank and in the centre of the line of beaters, while another officer with a set stood on high ground behind the line of guns.

133 animals were killed including 11 foxes. Following the shoot the public were asked to report to the police the finding of any dead foxes, squirrels, badgers, etc and also where live foxes had been seen frequently in a particular area so that they could be eliminated.

On November 5th a further control operation was mounted —this time covering the larger area of the urban district. Three teams each of four control officers were used in the surveying and killing of foxes only. The operation lasted a month after which one team was retained for a period of six months to act on sighting reports.

## ACTION BY THE MEDICAL AUTHORITIES

The divisional medical officer of health arranged treatment for Fritz's owners and, after rabies had been confirmed, about 50 people, mainly the children of Army personnel, were vaccinated. Fritz had had a great number of contacts with children and a few days before he became rabid had been taken to school. Although on a lead he had been fondled and stroked by a number of the children who were given sub cutaneous injections of the duck embryo dried killed virus vaccine for 14 days.

*34*

Generally speaking reactions were few but those that became evident were most marked in adults and were local reactions with, in a few cases, involvement of the associated lymph glands. Blood samples were taken from chosen adults over periods which varied from 7 days after the first injection to 4 weeks after the completion of the course. Examinations of samples showed that in the majority of cases a response was evident at the end of the full course of injections. In Mrs Hemsley's case it was fortunate that a very marked anti body response was obtained — she being the only person known to have been bitten by Fritz. This response was no doubt largely due to the fact that she had received the Semple Brain Tissue vaccine three years earlier after exposure to rabies in India.

The medical officer arranged for all hospitals and general practitioners to report all biting and scratching incidents to him direct. He in turn notified the divisional veterinary officer and the police. The latter investigated and traced the animals involved and also enquired whether the animal had been in the restricted area or near the commons between October 4th and 14th and whether it was showing any suspicious signs of rabies. The information was then passed to the veterinary officer. The animal concerned was examined immediately and again between the 7th and 10th day. If a restricted dog was involved, a further inspection was made on the 15th day. Owners of animals under enquiry were asked not to have them destroyed within 10 days of the incident, thus allowing time for any suspect symptoms to show.

During the period that restrictions were in force 208 enquiries into scratches and bites were made by the police mostly concerning dogs, but including a small number of other animals such as cats, squirrels and field mice. None of the incidents was found to have been caused by a rabid animal.

Veterinary surgeone practising in the district were kept informed by telephone and greatly helped allay public panic by keeping the disease risk in its proper perspective. They were asked to see that all dog and cat carcases within the district were incinerated and a list of suitable plants was compiled and circulated.

## STRAY DOGS

After October 19th all stray dogs brought to the police station were kept there. If not claimed by an owner within a week they were destroyed by an R.S.P.C.A. Inspector. Carcases were placed in plastic bags and burned in a near-by Army incinerator. Dogs claimed by their owners were placed under modified restrictions. During the early months, stray dogs were not allowed to be retained by their finders on a certificate but later this ruling was relaxed.

Four new kennels were provided and four wire mesh compounds erected — the latter to overcome difficulties experienced in handling and muzzling the dogs, there being no means of separating them. Equipment found necessary to meet the situation included woodwool for bedding, six muzzles of varying sizes, six pairs of strong gardening-type gloves, disinfectant, a plastic bucket, two pairs of overalls and a good supply of dog meal and tinned dog meat. This was all destroyed after restrictions were lifted.

Instructions issued to personnel handling stray dogs was as follows :—

(a) All dogs to be muzzled.

(b) Gloves after use, to be washed in a strong disinfectant solution and dried in the open air.

(c) Overalls and gloves to be worn while an officer handled dogs.

(d) After use muzzles to be well soaked in disinfectant and dried in the open air.

(e) Any personnel bitten or licked on the skin by a

*Plate 3*—East Sussex Anti-Rabies Squad. Diseases of Animals Inspectors and Co-ordinator in foreground.

*(Sussex Express & County Herald photo)*

Plate 4—The guns assemble for 'Rabies Shoot' on two commons near Camberley, Surrey, where a dog died of rabies. Wildlife is killed off to prevent the spread of the disease. (*Press Association photo*).

stray dog during handling to report the fact immediately.

(f) No stray dog to be allowed to escape.

It was originally intended that restrictions would last for eight months which meant that the dogs subject to the order would be released on June 14th. Unfortunately a further case of rabies was confirmed at Newmarket on 27th February, 1970 and the restriction period was extended to 12 months. Later, however, it was decided to reduce this to nine months and all dogs were released on July 14th.

Between that date and October 14th reports of biting and scratching incidents continued to be sent to the police who informed the animal's owner and asked him to notify them of any noticeable change in the temperament of the animal or any sign of ill-health within the next 10 days.

The Surrey Constabulary, who controlled the Camberley incident, concluded in a report issued later that prompt action in detaining and isolating a suspect animal is of the greatest importance in restricting the number of contacts and confining later action to as small an area as possible. Close liasion with medical and veterinary authorities is essential. Additional kennels and the equipment mentioned earlier in the chapter must be obtained early on and the public must be kept informed and, if rabies has spread over a wide area, it may be necessary to open advice centres and clinics.

Chapter Four

# RABIES AND QUARANTINE

## HISTORY IN BRITAIN

There is little doubt that Britain has only kept free from rabies for over half a century because of the strict quarantine regulations imposed on owners bringing pets home from abroad. Towards the end of the nineteenth century an attempt was made to reduce the incidence of the disease by an order prohibiting the landing of dogs except with a licence from the Board of Agriculture. Dogs had to be detained for six months on their owner's premises and muzzled when exercised. It was found impracticable to administer the order and in 1901 it was amended so that dogs landing from abroad had to be detained and isolated for six months under a veterinary surgeon's supervision. Within a year the contry was rabies free and remained so for a further sixteen years until a period from 1918-1922 when rabies spread from dogs thought to have been smuggled in by soldiers returning from the war. The period of quarantine has remained at six months apart from a reduction of two months during the First World War and a temporary lengthening to eight months following the Camberley incident.

## QUARANTINE ABROAD

The World Health Organisation Expert Committee on Rabies recommends that countries that are free of rabies should continue either to prohibit the importation of dogs and cats or subject then to a period of preferably four or more months quarantine at the port of entry. If the period is only four months, leashing and surveillance for a further two months are suggested.

When the Waterhouse Committee was gathering information for its Report of the Committee of Inquiry into Rabies, published in 1971, following the Camberley case, it found that Cyprus, Gibraltar and Hong Kong required a six month period with certain exemptions. Finland, Iceland, Norway and Sweden called for four months quarantine with varying qualifications. In Finland and Norway the four month period was followed by a two month special observation at destination, in case of animals arriving from countries where rabies were present. In Iceland quarantine was only asked for where rabies was present in the country of origin while in Sweden, animals from Denmark, Finland and Norway were exempt if accompanied by satisfactory health certificates and if they passed an inspection.

Denmark at one time had a quarantine station which was the main feature of its external rabies prevention measures. Control of traffic across land frontiers, especially during the height of the holiday season proved increasingly difficult for the police and, in 1969, when the station became infested with tics, it was closed. Denmark now limits imports to vaccinated animals, vaccinating them on arrival if necessary.

## QUARANTINE ESTABLISHMENTS

There are about fifty establishments in Britain authorised by Ministry of Agriculture veterinary officers to quarantine imported dogs and cats. These are regularly inspected to ensure that satisfactory security and welfare standards are maintained. The majority are situated within reasonable distances of a selected number of ports and airports where landings are allowed. A number of establishment owners are also approved as authorised carrying agents for transporting animals from port to kennels. Where this arrangement exists the procedure of making arrangements before applying for an import licence, is simplified.

Charges for quarantine vary according to the service provided but, like everything else, have been hit by inflation. For example, a new well equipped and heated kennels which opened about two years ago, charged £45.50 a month for dogs weighing 90 lbs or less and £60.00 for those weighing over 90 lbs. Cats cost £30.00 a month. Added to this were initial veterinary fees of £10.00 — £12.00 and carrying charges of 12p a mile.

A long established kennels in the south of England, at the time of writing, charges according to the breed of the dog ranging from £40.00 a month for an Afghan hound to £32.00 for a terrier. £25.00 a month is charged for a cat. If heating is required between October 1st and April 30th an extra charge of £5.00 a month for dogs and £3.50 a month for cats is incurred. Veterinary fees for inoculations amount to £16.00 and £19.00 respectively; the latter has increased considerably recently because an expensive injection against cat 'flu is now given. Fees for transporting animals are based on the distance from the port of arrival and are a fixed sum.

An enquiry into the rabid dog Fritz (see Chapter 3) has led to the conclusion that he might have become infected, not as was originally thought, before he left Germany, but in quarantine kennels in this country. During Fritz's period in quarantine, a collie in the same block of kennels, imported in April 1969 from India died after showing clinical signs of rabies for a week. The disease was subsequently confirmed after post mortem examination.

Fritz was released from quarantine on October 3rd 1969. On November 11th a labrador dog, referred to as Whiskey, who, throughout its quarantine period, was housed in the same compartment, and in the same block of kennels as Fritz, started showing signs of rabies. Within 48-hours Whiskey was unable to eat and was put down at its owner's request. Again rabies was confirmed following a post mortem.

Whiskey had been kept in a village near Hanover by his owners for six months before being brought to this country and was allowed to roam freely, being away from home for several hours on occasions. He came into quarantine on May 16th 1969. During the period 1st October 1968 to 30th April 1969 ten cases of rabies were confirmed in the area where he had lived previously — five in foxes, two in cats, one in a badger and two in unnamed species. The dog could therefore have been in contact with a rabid animal shortly before it left Germany.

The quarantine kennels where the three dogs who developed rabies, were housed, had been approved for over thirty years with accommodation for one hundred and eight dogs and twenty four cats. The report on the detailed investigation at the premises concluded that the construction of the kennels and the system of management was such as to prevent direct contact between dogs except as a deliberate action by a member of staff in contravention of the regulations. There was no reason to suspect that this had occurred, although the investigating team said they had insufficient confidence in the management of the kennels to rule out the possibility of direct transmission.

In the block of kennels where the three dogs were kept there were thirty individual compartments and an access passage. Seven outdoor exercise pens opened off the passage and one dog from each group of compartments was taken to the nearest pen for exercise and the door closed. After a period of exercise, the dogs were returned one by one to their compartments.

The possibility of indirect contact was also considered bearing in mind that the whole concept of quarantine kennel management had been based on the universal view that a bit from one animal to another was essential for the transmission of the disease. Indirect contact could have been brought about in the exercise runs and passages or through utensils, grooming tools etc. As there was no known record of an indirect transmission of rabies in dogs, little importance was placed on the risk from this type of contamination. Of the twenty seven cases of rabies that have occurred in quarantine there were four instances where dogs died from rabies following cases in the same kennels. As more than twenty years had elapsed since the last of these cases it is impossible to make a conclusive assessment. If there *had* been indirect contact between the three dogs, it would have been a rare occurrence.

## RECOMMENDATIONS OF WATERHOUSE COMMITTEE

The Committee, who held thirty five meetings and visited the World Health Organisation in Geneva as well as speaking to experts in five European countries on their experiences of rabies and programmes for prevention and control of the disease, was convinced that the retention and strengthening of the present quarantine system for dogs and cats was essential for the protection of the country from rabies.

They recommended that all imported dogs and cats should be vaccinated against the disease on arrival and re-vaccinated between fourteen and twenty eight days later. Where possible, after a 14-day isolation period, newly imported animals should be housed in the same block as other new arrivals and they should all use the same accommodation and exercise areas for the whole of the quarantine period. The sharing of accommodation should not be allowed except for a dam suckling a litter.

When discussing visiting by owners, having heard that dogs and cats normally take two weeks to settle down and bearing in mind the similar period of isolation following vaccination, the Committee recommended. that visiting should only begin at the end of a fortnight. It was opposed to the practice of an animal being brought to meet its owner in a special room. This should be done in the exercise run if the compartment is unsuitable.

The management of quarantine kennels is either in the hands of veterinary surgeons or lay owners but the veterinary surgeon who has to be appointed for each premises, has over-riding authority when dealing with disease and illness. The Committee saw no objections to ownership and general management being by lay men. All owners should be kept up to date with international development in the rabies field and information from official sources could usefully be circulated. Staff should receive instruction in the dangers of rabies and the security precautions necessary to prevent the spread of disease.

Discussing security the Committee recommended a suitable fence to prevent animals escaping and one gate for entrance and exit wide enough to allow entry of a vehicle, this to be closed while unloading is in progress.

Approved premises should be built in small self-contained blocks and within the quarantine perimeter there should be treatment rooms, washing, disinfection and incineration facilities for the exclusive use of animals undergoing quarantine. The compartments should be of the ''walk in'' type and have their interior surfaces faced with a smooth impervious material to a height that animals may be expected to reach by jumping.

All existing kennels should, within a period, be provided with individual exercise areas. All new premises must have them when built and they should be paved or surfaced so as to allow proper cleansing and disinfection. For existing kennels it was recommended that the same group of animals should always use the same run and records of how this was done should be kept.

The Committee considered it advisable for at least one inspection a year to be carried out by someone other than the regular veterinary advisor or inspector.

To be able to trace animals after release from quarantine, it was recommended that the address at which the animal will be kept should be left with the kennel proprietor and recorded at the appropriate Government department, to which any subsequent change of address of the owner, or the animal, or any change of ownership within nine months of its release from quarantine, should be notified. The owner should be given a copy of the animals record card kept during quarantine and advised to show it to any veterinary surgeon to whom it is taken for treatment. An appropriate disc should be worn by animals for nine months after release from quarantine.

If rabies is suspected in a dog or cat in quarantine, the animal should immediately be confined in isolation. The veterinary surgeon in control must notify the Ministry Veterinary Officer and, if the animal dies, its head and neck should be sent for rabies diagnosis. Dogs and cats released from quarantine within 14 days preceding the first signs of rabies in a quarantined animal, should be returned and the quarantine period extended for those and the animals still on the premises.

Most of the more stringent requirements recommended by the Waterhouse Committee have been put into effect since 1972 or earlier. The only one not yet fully implemented relates to individual exercise runs. As this required major reconstruction in some kennels, a transitional period of seven years, expirin in September 1979, was allowed, it being expected that in those cases where it was found impractical to comply, the premises would cease to be used for quarantine and in future cater solely for native animals.

## QUARANTINE STATION AT HEATHROW AIRPORT

Described as one of the most comprehensively designed and constructed premises in Europe, if not the rest of the world, the new Animal Quarantine Station at Heathrow

*Plate* 5—A Ministry of Agricultural divisional officer from Worcester holds up a vixen — first bag of the 'rabies shoot' on Camberley common. (*Press Association photo*).

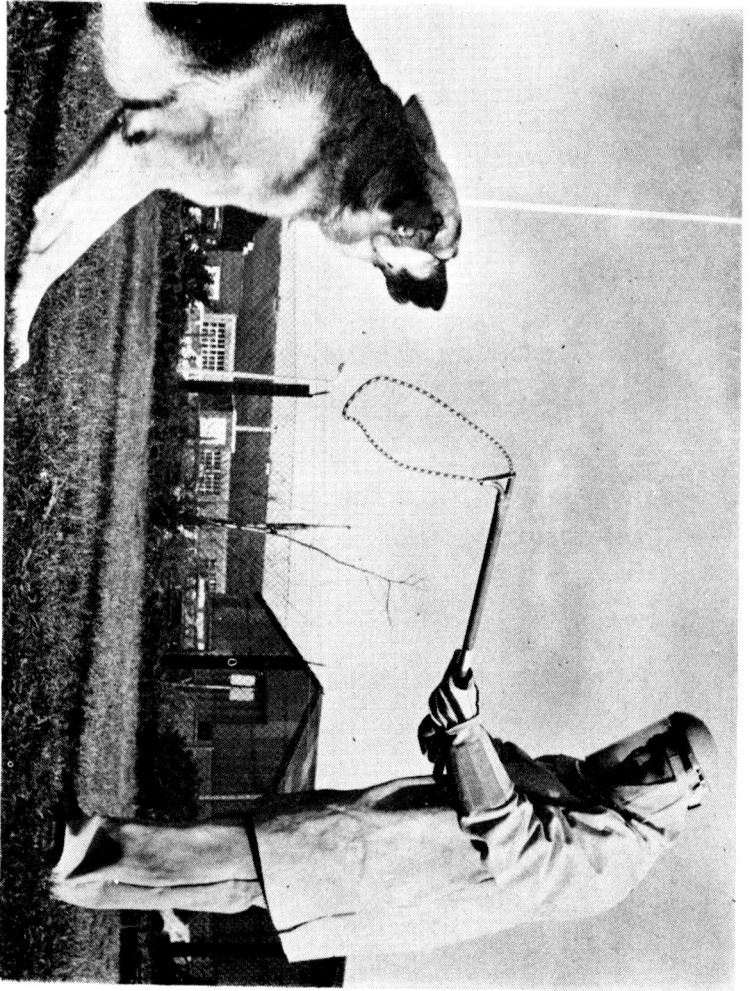

Plate 6—Newhaven Harbour Policeman in Anti-Rabies Suit. (*Photo C. G. Casswell*).

Airport, was officially opened by H.R.H. The Princess Anne, Mrs Mark Philips, G.C.V.O. on February 7th 1977.

Prior to the opening of the new centre, facilities at Heathrow for the importation or trans-shipment of animals were provided in an animal hostel run by the R.S.P.C.A. Some eighty per cent of all animals passing through the hostel were "in trans-shipment" and in 1970 no fewer than sixty five thousand mammals in this category were handled. The extent to which Heathrow is used for the importation of dogs and cats is borne out by the 1969 figures which show that of the total arriving in this country by air, ninety per cent landed at Heathrow.

The Rabies (Importation of Dogs, Cats and Other Mammals) Order 1974, required the provision of "secure holding facilities" at approved air and sea ports. It was a result of this legislation that the City of London decided to build a completely new animal quarantine station at Heathrow. Costing nearly three quarters of a million pounds the facilities meet the most stringent health and security arrangements.

The reception area was designed so that lorries and vans could drive inside the building and then be enclosed by electrically operated doors, to ensure that any animal which might have escaped from its crate inside the lorry does not later escape outside the quarantine station. Alarm systems, in case of fire and/or escape of one of the animals, have been installed. Magnetic and electrically controlled doors to pens and corridors enable staff to control the animals more easily in emergencies.

The station includes twenty six dog runs, sixteen cat pens, four ape rooms, four lion dens and eleven bird rooms as well as facilities for much larger animals. Outdoor fenced runs, all within a high perimeter fence, have been provided for animals staying more than a few hours. At the centre of the building are the food stores and preparation rooms, a surgery, a post mortem room, disinfecting facilities, a crate washing room and a large incinerator for the disposal of all bedding, carcases, etc.

Specialised equipment, such as the ultra-violet air sterilising system for the bird section, which prevents contaminated air reaching the outside of the building, is used where necessary. For the larger or more dangerous animals, there are four specially constructed cages, fitted with movable walls to assist re-crating and other procedures.

The whole animal quarantine complex, which it is estimated will cost over a quarter of a million pounds to run, is part of the veterinary sector of the City of London Health Department and is under day-to-day control of its veterinary officer, Geoffrey Wiggins. In addition to four qualified veterinarians, three management personnel and seventeen animal attendants are employed. Staff wear protective clothing inside the station and, before entering or leaving the changing room, must walk through a shallow pool of disinfectant. The welfare of animals during loading, unloading and in transit is carried out by the veterinary sector.

The emphasis at the new station is on speed of transportation and it is well equipped as the country's principal port of entry into Britain for most livestock. Now that the threat of rabies entering the country appears more likely, the need for a specially designed quarantine station to cope with the increasing volume of traffic, has been fully met at Heathrow.

## SAD END FOR GREEK SEA DOG

Christmas 1977 saw the sad demise of a Greek sea dog, Lakis, who was marooned aboard a ship-wrecked freighter in St Ives Bay. The dog's adventures began when the Greek vessel Fastbird II sheltering in rough weather, broke loose from her anchor and ran aground on the sand.

At low tide when she was high and dry, the crew were taken off by the local lifeboat. Lakis was left on board while officials tried to discover his owner. The skipper said the animal was already on the ship when he took over and it didn't belong to him. As no-one could be found to pay for the dog to be quarantined, it was decided he must be destroyed.

But the tide rose and high winds lifted the boat back into the sea. Before it was dashed against the rocks a mine-sweeper managed to get a line aboard but while towing it towards Milford Haven, the line snapped and Lakis was once more left in charge of the deserted ship.

A request from William Allen, director of Milford Haven port health authority for someone to play Santa Claus and take over responsibility for Lakis was answered by dozens of pet lovers but despite this, he was put down on orders from the local diseases of animals authority.

*Chapter Five*

# RABIES AND WILD ANIMALS

In Britain — in bats — in skunks — in rodents —in foxes — in other species — wild life protection.

## IN BRITAIN

There are few known facts about rabies among wild life in the United Kingdom. The only two recorded out-breaks were among deer — one in 1856 in Yorkshire and the other thirty years later in Richmond Park. It is thought that on both occasions, the disease was introduced into herds by rabid dogs.

In both cases it was reported that the deer acted like rabid dogs, foaming at the mouth, attempting to bite each other and tearing at the hair and flesh. The 1887 Agricultural Report concerning the Richmond Park outbreak stated that there was no penetration of the skin by the teeth but sores were produced and saliva left on the skin. It was noticed on a number of occasions that a bitten animal licked the sore — no doubt to soothe the irritation.

To test whether the disease could be passed by a bite, a rabid doe was placed in a shed with a healthy buck which had previously been isolated from the infected herds. Immediately the two animals were placed together, the doe flew at the buck like a dog and bit it on the ears and neck. The buck was regularly examined and on the 19th day showed signs of rabies. It became furious and died within a very short space of time. This experiment conclusively proved that rabies can be conveyed by the bite of a rabid herbivore to another animal and was the means of transmitting the infection among the deer herds. As the animal

*48*

has no upper incisors, this method of inoculation must have been somewhat uncertain and no doubt accounted for the slow progress of disease among the herd, a feature which puzzled the experts of the day.

Of 3,056 recorded deaths of rabies in the U.K. in animals between 1886 and 1903, 259 were among deer. In the considerable amount of literature on hunting and the pursuit of game, there are no references to the dangers of rabies among game animals, although as long ago as 1420, Edward, Duke of York clearly described the disease and its transmission among hounds.

## IN BATS

A number of the various species of bat can transmit rabies. A particular problem exists in Latin America where the vampire bat is said to have accounted for half a million deaths annually among cattle in the 1960's. It is probable that the vampire's establishment in this area coincided with the introduction of large numbers of domestic and farm animals. Vaccination of cattle, a move prompted by the serious economic losses from wholesale deaths, has no doubt helped the situation. The toll from rabies is still thought to be serious, many cases going unreported. Vampires are also a threat to humans who can become infected when their blood is sucked while asleep.

Bats *can* die of rabies but appear to carry it for a considerable and, some think, indefinite period. Control is being improved through the use of anti-coagulant drugs. These are injected into cattle in controlled doses that are safe to them but which prove fatal to vampire bats feeding on them sometime afterwards. The bat's saliva also contains an anti-coagulant substance, which prevents the blood clotting. Without the substance being introduced into bovines, a good supply of blood is ensured, but when it is, the blood is lethal to the bat. The vampire bat, which if imported into the U.K. must be quarantine for life, lives entirely on blood.

The Florida yellow bat carry rabies in the U.S.A. and further south in Brazil, the virus was first isolated from the spear-nosed bat during the First World War. In the U.S.A. over half of the known species of bat have been found to be carriers of rabies and the disease, first confirmed in the U.S.A. as being bat borne in 1953 has, since then, been isolated in the animal in all but four States.

There have been fears that rabies could be introduced into the U.K. by the bat. Relatively few cases of bat rabies have been reported from Europe, all in insectivorous types. Research into one species, the Mouse-eared bat shows a strong possibility that they migrate to Britain from the Continent. Although it is thought that the chances of rabies being introduced here in this way are slight, it is wise to note that bats frequently become paralysed in the early stages of the disease. In that state it is extremely dangerous to humans should they pick them up or to animals who try and investigate them.

As a safeguard against possible infection from freeze-dried bats imported into this country for exhibition in museums, because this method favours the survival of the rabies virus, the Waterhouse Committee in its report warned that the handling of such specimens may involve some danger, and suggested they be treated with care.

*IN SKUNKS*

Skunks are responsible for the greatest number of cases among wild life in the U.S.A. The disease in this animal has concerned the American Health authorities for more than three quarters of a century. Both the spotted and striped skunk are involved and these animals caused sixteen human deaths in one year in the Arkansas Valley areas. In California in 1967 ninety three out of one hundred and eighteen cases in animals, involved skunks while a year later in Canada twenty five per cent of the cases in wild life occurred in the same animal. Rabies in dogs in the U.S.A. is declining while the disease in skunks is increasing and spreading into new areas.

## IN RODENTS

Rabies has been established in a number of species of rodents in various parts of the world. In 1970 Czechoslovakian research workers claimed to have confirmed the disease in both field mice and rats over a large part of their country. This was later thought to be merely a rabies virus which could not immediately cause the disease in animals such as foxes but after passing serially through mice, could become virulent enough to change from a non-overt to overt form of the disease.

This and similar non-overt types could act as a wild life reservoir of disease not apparent but which might under certain circumstances change to recognizable rabies.

Many European countries are concerned about the chances of rats and mice carrying rabies and are engaged in research into the possibilities. In the past, when ships were commonly infested with rats, particularly the black rat, a known carrier of plague, sailors were often bitten; but there is no known case of rabies being contracted from rodents aboard ship. Modern vessels have little harbourage for rats, rat proofing has improved and vessels are inspected twice a year and issued with a 'rat free' certificate or, if rats are found, treated by poisoning or fumigation.

## IN FOXES

The publicity campaign mounted by the Government in 1976 designed to make the public fully aware of the dangers from rabies, was prompted by its spread across Europe towards the north coast of France. The carrier of the disease in this area is the red fox. This animal is the main transmitter of epidemic and endemic wild life rabies in Europe. Being highly susceptible and known to excrete the virus in its saliva, the fox, because of its high population density and turnover, ensures the maintenance of the infection despite its fatal course in the animal.

Fluctuations in the incidence of rabies among foxes in Europe are related to the density of the animals's population. The more foxes that exist in an area, the more frequent are the opportunities for contact and passing of the virus. In the current upsurge in rabies in Europe, the only cases occurring in animals other than foxes were as a consequence of contact with them.

The fox population in north west Europe has increased considerably in recent years, largely due to the cessation of hunting during the Second World War. Populations tend to peak every two or three years and rabies is most prevalent at those times. Maximum spread of fox rabies occurs in the spring during the mating season and again in the autumn when young foxes leave the vixen in search of their own territory. Areas where the fox population has been thinned by death from rabies are re-stocked from neighbouring areas. It is also thought there may be a two or three fold increase in the size of litters which helps compensate for the losses.

At the beginning of the Second World War many cases of rabies in foxes were reported from Poland and ten years later the disease had spread to Czechoslovakia and Austria. By 1960 it had reached the Rhine and after a temporary halt has progressed westwards virtually uninterrupted at a rate of between twenty and forty km a year. Established in Belgium and Luxembourg in 1967, it had reached France a year later and by 1975 had been confirmed in the Pas de Calais area.

During the years 1968 - 1973 of nine and a half thousand confirmed cases of animal rabies in France, no fewer than seven and a half thousand were in foxes. The fact that during the period 1969 - 1973 the total of nineteen thousand confirmed animal rabies cases in the U.S.A. included only three and a half thousand in foxes, underlines the extent to which the latter animal is the principal carrier of the disease in Europe.

The fox adapts easily to its environment and in Britain commonly lives in scrubland, and on the edges of woods and forests, making occasional runs into more open country looking for food. It has a varied diet and can exist on insects and vegetation.

In recent years the fox has been seen in increasing numbers in urban areas. As long as food is readily available it usually keeps to a defined area some twelve miles from its birth place or previous "home range". It may have more than one "earth" within a home range and the latter may overlap depending on the type of countryside involved. Dog foxes spend a great part of the time away from their earths in the summer, but research has shown that the species do not normally travel great distances. Exceptional travel has been noted in France where railway lines may have been followed.

Partial control of rabies among foxes may be achieved by gassing vixens and cubs in their burrows. The disease appears to die out when the density of the fox falls below about one per square kilometre. This is not desirable as a depleted area is often re-colonised from more densely populated adjoining ones. The aim with this type of control is to reduce the population level to a point where the spread of rabies is greatly diminished but to one whereby the home ranges of the animals that are left, still cover the area adequately to ward off new arrivals.

Continued gassing of fox dens often causes foxes to avoid them for whelping so that the method can never bring about extinction of the species. The success of gassing also depends on the co-operation of farmers game wardens and hunters in locating the burrows.

Fox density is monitored in Europe by the use of hunting records, and it has been shown that in areas where control was by hunting a "bag" of about one fox per square km was obtained. In areas where gassing had taken place this had reduced to 0.2 foxes per square km. In those countries where an annual estimate of the fox population is made, it may be possible to forecast the potential danger and intensity of rabies outbreaks.

Denmark has achieved some success in halting the progress of rabies from Germany. The disease crossed the border in 1964 and at that time control measures consisted of gassing burrows and the laying of poison bait using strychnine nitrate very selectively in a strip of land across Southern Jutland reaching 20 kilometeres north of the last recorded outbreak. Within a second 20 kilometre zone to the north, premiums were paid for all foxes shot.

Control of rabies in foxes by vaccination is being tried experimentally. The animal has proved more amenable than any other wild life species to oral immunization which at the present time, is not acceptable in this country because the required dosage and length of time immunity would be provided are not well known enough.

The use of vaccine in baits is being investigated and agricultural officials in the state of Lower Saxony have begun an experiment in inoculating fox cubs with anti-rabies vaccines. Some years ago the gassing of foxes was banned in Germany when an appeals court reacted to pressure from animal protection groups — Lower Saxony decided they could not remain inactive and set in motion the field experiment in a state owned forest and two other limited areas.

Young foxes are caught at night in tubular wire mesh traps, inoculated, marked on the ear and released. The programme will be spread over three years and it is estimated that about one hundred foxes a year will be dealt with. At the end of the period a watch will be kept for any decline in rabies outbreaks in the area.

The makers of the vaccine claim complete immunity in

*Plate 7*—Caesar's Camp, the quarantine kennels at Folkstone, Kent. Rabid dogs have been destroyed here.

**Plan of front part of Home Range block of the QUARANTINE KENNELS, CAESER'S CAMP, FOLKESTONE**

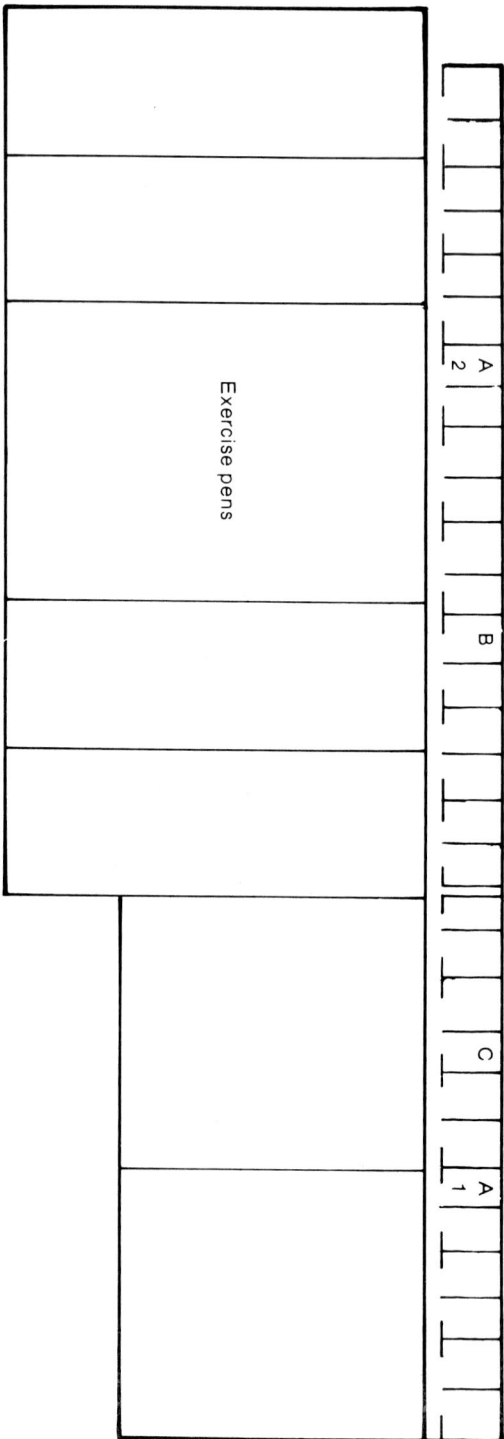

Exercise pens

A2    B    C    A1

A. Pen occupied by collie which died of rabies in quarantine on 26th July, 1969. It was moved from pen A1 to A2 on 22nd July, 1969.

B. Pen occupied by the dog which died of rabies in Camberley, Surrey, on 18th October, 1969.

C. Pen occupied by dog which was proved positive for rabies on 15th November, 1969.

Note 1. Dividing walls between exercise pens are of concrete block to 4 feet with double chain link fencing, 4 in. apart, up to 7 feet with an internal overhang.

2. Floors of all exercise runs are of concrete.

(Reproduced with the permission of the Controller of Her Majesty's Stationery Office.)

*Figure 3*—Quarantine kennels at Ceasar's Camp, Folkestone. (Plan).

the dog for one year, limited protection in the second year and slight resistance to infection in the third. It is not known what effect it will have on the fox.

Radio-telemetry is being used to determine movement amongst foxes. In Britain the Ministry of Agriculture's Animal Health Division has sent a research team to mid-Wales where foxes are being caught, fitted with collars to which are attached tiny radio transmitters and then released. These are being used to log the habits and movements of the animal. Each transmitter, which is about the size of a packet of ten cigarettes, gives off a signal which is picked up by a receiver in a land rover. The latter is light enough for Ministry staff to carry should they have to follow a fox on foot, and can be tuned in to a particular fox. One has already been followed for thirty miles before it mated.

The research is designed to show how large a control area would have to be set up if rabies in foxes had to be dealt with. Similar work is being carried out in the Netherlands and is being co-ordinated by the World Health and the Food and Agricultural Organisations.

## *IN OTHER SPECIES*

In certain of the Caribbean Islands, such as Puerto Rico and Cuba, rabies has been introduced inadvertently by man. Here the mongoose was imported to control rats and snakes on the sugar plantations. In the late '40's' it became infected with rabies, possibly through migrating bats. It now presents a major health problem to the authorities since it has become a persistent reservoir of the disease, has no natural competitors and attacks man as well as domestic animals.

In Europe rabies has been found in roedeer, badgers, martens and polecats, while in Canada coyotes, wolves and lynx have been affected in large numbers. The virus has also been discovered in a number of the rodent species such as hare, rabbit, squirrel, mouse and vole. In the Lebanon rats were, in 1969, high up on the list of carriers of the disease.

## *WILD LIFE PROTECTION*

Attempts to control rabies in wild life inevitably lead to criticism principally on moral and emotional grounds. Extermination except by poisoning is costly and the latter, like trapping, can endanger humans and domestic animals. The value of such control measures is not always positive and tends to upset the balance among the various species.

A number of successful programmes have been carried out notably one in Alberta in 1952 when nearly one hundred thousand animals including foxes, coyotes, wolves, lynx, bears and skunks were killed. The disease was thought to have been imported from the North-West Territory by the fox and was transmitted to dogs, wolves and farm livestock. Two hundred people were vaccinated after bites and scratches.

Stray dogs were destroyed, all dogs were compulsorily vaccinated and professional trappers drastically reduced the numbers of foxes, coyotes and wolves by trapping, gassing and baiting. Rabies disappeared from Alberta and while the number of animal deaths might have shocked an ecologist, the action probably prevented rabies from becoming endemic.

*Chapter six*

## RABIES AND VACCINATION

History in humans — personal experiences — recent developments — in animals — types of vaccine used.

### *HISTORY IN HUMANS*

Research into vaccination against rabies was initiated by the famous French chemist, Louis Pasteur, who was the first to show that the disease is caused by a virus present in the spinal cord and brain. He also demonstrated that it was possible to "fix" the virus by passing it through a series of rabbits and monkeys and establishing that it became stronger at each passage with a progressively shorter incubation period. The fixed virus of the rabbit and monkey was found to be less potent when passed through the dog.

When preparing his first anti-rabies vaccine, Pasteur injected the virus grown in the rabbit's nerve tissues, beginning with doses of killed virus and ending with fresh tissue containing live virus. The vaccine was injected into dogs daily and it was found that immunity to rabies was built up — even inoculation into the area of the brain failed to produce the disease. There were however some failures classified by Pasteur as "accidents".

The first time Pasteur considered using the vaccine on a human was in July 1885 when nine year old Joseph Meister was brought in after having been bitten on the hand and legs by a dog suspected of being rabid. Fortunately the more serious wounds had been cauterized a few hours after the incident.

In company with two medical colleagues, **Pasteur**

examined the boy and the extensive range of the wounds led them to believe that it was impossible to save him. Pasteur decided, in desperation, to use the vaccine that had been partially successful in immunizing dogs. Three months later, it was safe to report that Joseph was completely cured.

Pasteur effected a similar cure in a shepherd boy who had been bitten by a dog after trying to save a number of younger boys from its attack. As a result of these successes, the method was adopted widely in practice.

Pasteur's method was modified a few years later by Fermi who used phenol to thin out the virus instead of relying, as the former did, on the drying of the infected spinal chords. In 1973 the World Health Organisation advised discontinuance of this method in man because it involved the use of residual live virus.

Fermi's method was further modified in 1919 when Semple, in addition to phenol, used a temperature of 37 C. Sixteen years later it was discovered that it was better to use a sheep's or rabbit's brain than the spinal cord. These later Semple-type vaccines employ completely killed virus and have been widely used for a number of years, although they have given rise to serious side effects and occasionally death. For this reason they are not used on people likely to be exposed to risk at work but reserved for use on those already bitten by a rabid animal.

It is believed that myelin in the nerve tissues can give rise to one of the more serious side effects — encephalo-myelitis which, even if the patient survives, may leave a form of paralysis or nervous disorder. To counteract this, vaccines were later developed from the nerve tissue of very young animals in which the myelin is, as yet, un-developed. Particularly successful was the Fuenzilada type developed in 1955 and prepared from suckling mice under nine days old, a vaccine widely used in Latin America with good results but still leaving side effects of the nervous system in some cases.

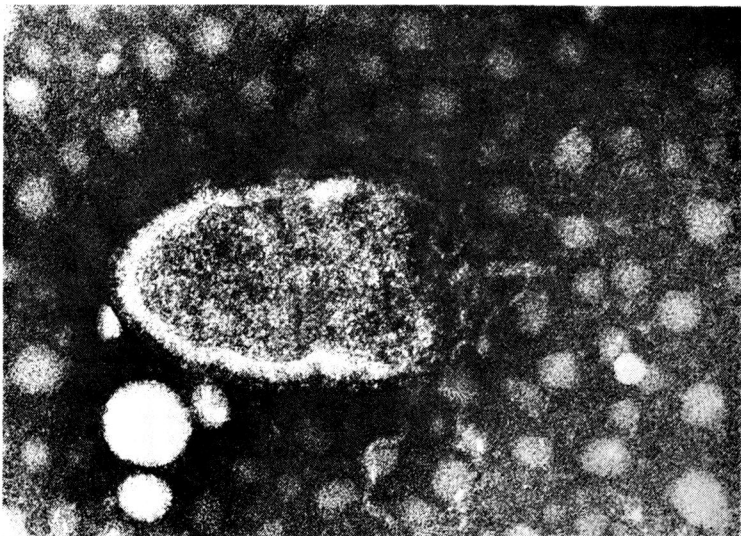

*Plate* 8(top)—Rabies vaccine virus from photograph taken at the Clinical Research Centre, Harrow. (*WHO photo*).

*Plate* 8(bottom)—Chloroform Chamber for destruction of cats and other small animals.

*Plate* 9—Dr. L. Andral plots the latest rabies outbreak on a wall map of France. (*Farmers Weekly photo*).

## PERSONAL EXPERIENCES

An Englishman on business in India was bitten on the back of the leg in Chittagong and after difficulty in obtaining treatment finally received the full course of injections at a British High Commission hospital in Delhi. He survived but has had nervous trouble ever since and needed a three-year period of follow-up treatment in London. He spoke of the side effects as indescribable.

Clifford Bland, a 64 year old Lewes man, was living in Malaga in 1968 when he was bitten by a cat. He reported the incident to the Spanish Ministry of Agriculture who instructed him to buy a course of Semple type vaccines, for treatment by a doctor in his home. He was forced to stay in bed for more than a month and given sixteen injections in the stomach. He became very depressed, fearing that he might have contracted rabies.

To build him up for loss of weight, he was given a series of thirty vitamin injections in the rectum. The treatment left him in a nervous state for more than six months after the incident. Mr Bland told the writer that all dogs in Spain must be vaccinated against rabies. The owner, who is given a certificate by the veterinary surgeon, takes it to the local town hall where he is issued with a disc to attach to the animal's collar certifying that it has been vaccinated.

The Spanish authorities deal ruthlessly with stray dogs. These are fed on meat poisoned with strychnine and left to die in agony sometimes exhibiting symptoms which could be confused with rabies.

On his return to England, Mr Bland's experiences were publicised as he felt strongly that rabies was not being treated seriously here. He appeared on local T.V. advocating that persons who smuggled animals into the country should automatically be given the same course of injections he received in Spain!

Since 1960 the most commonly used vaccine has been one produced from duck embryo. This vaccine was found to be much safer than those deriving from nerve tissues although there is a high incidence of short term side effects and doubts have been expressed as to its efficiency as an immunising agent. It is thought that anti-bodies build up faster with the duck embryo vaccine but usually at a lower level than in people vaccinated with the nerve tissue type. Duck embryo vaccines are now used for post exposure treatment, usually requiring a minimum of fourteen daily doses in the stomach—this area of the body was chosen as being the only area capable of withstanding that number of uncomfortable swellings. They are also employed for protecting people whose work may bring them into contact with rabid animals. In the latter case, two injections in the arm at six weekly intervals are followed by a booster dose six months later, and a further booster, which will last two-three years, a year after that.

Research has continued to find better vaccines with improved purification techniques particularly in the field of cell culture. Kissling in 1958 grew rabies virus in cultures of nerve-cells and in Canada and Russia immunisation agents have been developed from cells in baby hampster kidneys. These have been used extensively on humans in Russia.

Research in the U.S.A. and Western Europe has concentrated on producing H D C S vaccine from human diploid cell substrates. Problems existed with possible changes within the structure e.g. cancer producing matter, but determined efforts by academics working with chemists have, particularly in France, overcome these difficulties. The vaccine produced appears safe and gives a strong immunity. Trials have shown that there is a good anti-body reaction even after small doses. Although relatively high in cost, its freedom from side effects is a considerable advantage over similar earlier techniques. In addition, vaccinated subjects may now with safety donate blood for producing human anti-rabies serum.

## Rabies and Vaccination

The value of the use of serum was demonstrated in 1954 when, after twenty nine people were bitten by a rabid wolf in an Iranian village, those given serum *and* vaccine showed a better improvement rate than those treated with vaccine only. The H D C S vaccine produced at the Institute Merieux in France underwent two years of trials in this country. Over two hundred people were vaccinated through the Medical Research Council before, in June 1976, the Minister of State for Health, in a written answer in the House of Commons, said that the results of the trials had enabled his department to licence the vaccine for use in this country as a preventive measure for people at special risk. That year the Medical Research Council began experiments which it is hoped will confirm that the vaccine is also effective for the treatment of people who have been bitten by a rabid animal.

The vaccine, which is being stored at the Central Public Health Laboratory at Colindale is to be used to immunise veterinary surgeons, kennel maids at quarantine kennels, animal handlers at zoos, customs and excise staff and diseases of animals inspectors. The vaccine can be given in a single dose or up to four doses spread over several days, depending on the type of risk.

Tests carried out by the World Health Organisation doctors have confirmed claims made by the Merieux Institute that this vaccine is effective in people bitten by animals affected with the disease. The vaccine is described by Doctor Koprowski in the Journal of the American Medical Association as a "major break-through".

It was tested on forty five Persian people who were bitten by six rabid dogs and two rabid wolves between June 1975 and January 1976. After six injections of the vaccine and one of rabies serum, no patient developed the disease and none suffered any side effects in the process.

*IN ANIMALS*

Opinions on the effectiveness of anti-rabies vaccines on

*61*

animals are mixed. The use of them in the U.K. is prohibited under the Rabies Act 1974 (with the exception of animals in quarantine) because the possible excretion of virus in the saliva may represent a public health hazard. Live vaccines are potentially dangerous in pregnant animals, those under three months of age and in species in which their safety is as yet unproven.

Much also depends on the animal's state of health, differences in the quality of available vaccines, the varied response of individual animals and the amount of rabies virus absorbed should the animal subsequently be bitten by an affected animal.

Many cases of rabies among animals have been recorded despite their being previously vaccinated. In England a dog which died in quarantine in 1968 had been vaccinated twice in the country of origin the previous year. In the last case of rabies in this country, which concerned a terrier-cross dog imported from Pakistan and which developed the disease three months after release from quarantine kennels at Newmarket, the animal had been vaccinated three times. The only case of the disease in a cat in quarantine since 1922 was in an animal that had been vaccinated previously.

The Waterhouse Committee recommended that dogs and cats should be vaccinated at least fourteen days but not more than 12 months before entry except in cases where it is prohibited in the country of origin. Even if this has been done the animal is still subjected to vaccination on entry to the U.K. and again after one month in quarantine to extend immunity to any animal that may not have responded to the first vaccination.

On the other hand there have been successes with mass vaccination of dogs. In 1948, after rabies had been building up alarmingly in Memphis, Tennessee for two years an intensive canine vaccination campaign succeeded in immunising twenty three thousand dogs in about a week. This despite compliance being voluntary and the cost — one dollar per dog. From early April, the time of the campaign, to the end of July the number of rabid animals and persons treated fell from fourteen and ten respectively, to nil.

A successful campaign was also carried out in Malaya after the Japanese occupation of the Second World War. Explosive outbreaks were brought under control by British veterinary officers.

When the Waterhouse Committee visited countries on the Continent to investigate rabies control procedure, they found that the Federal State of Germany allowed prophylactic vaccination after establishing that vaccination of dogs with a live vaccine did not produce a communicable, symptomless form of rabies in some vaccinated animals.

At the time, vaccination of dogs and cats in France in infected areas was voluntary although the Prefect of an area had powers to make it compulsory. In Switzerland where, because of its borders with other countries, it was found impossible to limit the passage of dogs and cats, particularly for short periods during holiday seasons, a comprehensive vaccination programme was brought in. The total dog population must be vaccinated every year with an inactivated vaccine or every two years with a live one. Dogs and cats entering the country must have been vaccinated not less than thirty days and not more than a year, before entry. The Swiss allow the re-entry of their own dogs on presentation of a valid vaccination certificate.

In the South Jutland area of Denmark where rabies crossed the border in 1964, all dogs have to be vaccinated every three years with a vaccine produced in Canada from a pig tissue culture. Denmark's government meets the bill for the material and the vaccination fee.

*TYPES OF VACCINE USED*

Vaccine used on animals include chick embryo types. The low egg passage Flury strain was found more effective than vaccines from infected brains of sheep or goats and resulted in one hundred per cent protection of dogs given the rabies virus over three years after receiving a single dose of the vaccine.

This and high egg passage vaccine were used on a large number of various ages and breeds but have produced undesirable reactions in many cases especially when repeated injections have been given.

Newer and safer types of animal vaccines include cell culture vaccines and those provided from suckling mouse brains.

There are advantages and disadvantages with both the live and inactivated types of vaccine. It is important for veterinarians to test the chosen vaccine lot and assure that it has been shipped and stored properly. An ideal type of vaccine is one that is safe to use in any species of animal with a dependable protection, is economical and will remain potent for at least twelve hours without refrigeration.

Vaccination in animals does not pose the same problems as it does in man for those exposed to rabies are rarely, if ever, treated but instead, put down. The World Health Organisation consider it should form part of all long range rabies control programmes and that dog owners should be encouraged to have their pets vaccinated as soon as possible after the age of three months with the exception of countries which are free from the disease. In these cases a policy of import control and quarantine is recommended. Only in the event of an outbreak of rabies in the U.K., would compulsory vaccination be used.

## Chapter Seven

# RABIES AND THE LAW

Importation Order 1974 — pets on boats — boarding documents — crating of animals on aircraft — offences against the Order.

## IMPORTATION ORDER 1974

Persons wishing to bring an animal into the U.K. after living abroad, those thinking of taking one on holiday overseas and returning with it, and others who may buy one in a foreign country or take pity on a stray puppy or kitten seen on their travels and want to bring it home, should be aware of the strict provision of the import regulations with which they will have to comply.

The Rabies (Importation of Dogs, Cats and Other Mammals) Order of 1974 forbids the landing in Great Britain of an animal brought from outside that area except when a licence has been obtained in advance. The prohibition does not apply to an animal imported from Northern Ireland, the Irish Repulic, the Channel Isles or the Isle of Man, unless it has been earlier brought to those countries from elsewhere and had not undergone at least six months quarantine before being landed in Great Britain.

Apart from dogs and cats, the order applies to a large number of familiar as well as lesser known exotic pets and includes rabbits, mice, hamsters, gerbils, guinea pigs and chinchillas among the former and bears, wallabies, kangaroos, marmosets and bush babies among the latter. All these species are subject to six months quarantine, the vampire bat being the only mammal that must remain in such circumstances for life.

Apart from vessels and aircraft diverted for safety or other exceptional circumstances, importations are only

*65*

allowed at a restricted number of ports and airports which are equipped for handling animal traffic of this kind. These are :—

| *PORTS* | *AIRPORTS* |
|---|---|
| Dover | Birmingham |
| Folkestone | Edinburgh |
| Harwich | Gatwick |
| Hull | Glasgow |
| Liverpool | Heathrow |
| London (including Tilbury) | Leeds |
| Newhaven | Manchester |
| International Hoverport, Ramsgate. | Prestwick |
| Southampton | |

## PETS ON BOATS

A licence is not necessary in the case of an animal landed at a British port or airport if it is to be re-exported within forty eight hours. It can then only be moved within the port or airport by an authorised carrier and, if it remains for more than four hours, must be kept in the authorised holding premises provided.

What does a prospective pet owner have to do when he wants to import an animal from abroad? He must first reserve a place in approved quarantine accommodation. The Ministry of Agriculture and Fisheries at Tolworth, Surrey hold a list of some fifty approved premises that board dogs and cats. He will also have to arrange for an authorised carrier to meet the boat or aircraft on arrival and transport the animal to its kennels or cattery. A number of owners of quarantine establishments are also appointed as authorised carriers and it will simplify the procedure if one of these can be found. The Ministry also hold a list of research establishments and acclimatisation centres which have been aproved under the Exotic Animals (Importation) Order for dealing with animals other than cats and dogs. Anyone wishing to import such an animal is well advised to make enquiries well in advance so that a suitable premises can be located.

Having gone through these preliminaries, a licence for importation must be obtained from the Animal Health Division of the Ministry of Agriculture at Hook Rise South, Tolworth, Surbiton, Surrey. The applicant will note from the conditions attaching to the licence that the animal must be vaccinated on arrival and again four weeks later, and that should it share accommodation with an animal or animals that subsequently develop rabies it may have to be slaughtered. If it dies in quarantine, any action necessary to find out whether or not it was infected with rabies at the time of death, may be taken and the remains may be disposed of as the Ministry thinks fit.

## BOARDING DOCUMENTS

In an effort to try and reduce the number of illegally landed animals, particularly where the owner alleges that he boarded a vessel or aircraft quite openly and travelled with the animal, the Ministry, on January 1st 1975, introduced what is known as a "boarding document". Virtually an animal passport, the document is issued at the same time as the licence and must be produced by the animal's owner or agent to the shipper or airline he and the animal are travelling with, as an indication that a licence has been issued.

The new arrangements were made known to all shippers and airlines involved in transporting animals to this country and they were asked to co-operate by ensuring that no arrangements are made, or animals allowed to embark, unless the boarding document concerning the importation is available when an animal is taken on board for transport to the U.K.

The document states the place of landing, number of animals involved, destination, name of the carrier, identification of the animals and the purpose of importation.

## CRATING OF ANIMALS ON AIRCRAFT

To further reduce the number of animals being illegally landed, the Ministry tightened the import licence conditions again when, in August 1975, they wrote to all air line operators telling them that as from September 1st 1975 animals may only travel to this country by air as freight in an approved container. They would be listed on the aircraft's manifest and under no circumstances allowed to travel as accompanied passenger baggage or in the cabin compartment of an aircraft.

The reasons given for the change were to make sure that all animals landing in Great Britain remained under Custom control until cleared for release on production of an appropriate import licence or documentary evidence of a genuine trans-shipment arrangement. It would also prevent owners of unlicensed animals from stating that there had been no attempt to smuggle an animal and that they were unaware that an offence had been committed.

The "travelling as freight" procedure was also made to apply to an animal landing at an airport and going forward on another flight and to one taken by road, rail or air from the airport or port for exportation. There are as yet no similar provisions relating to animals imported by ship and in practice many cross-channel ferries do provide suitable containers for housing animals in transit.

A requirement of the Importation Order that is not generally known relates to animals taken to a place outside the British Isles. Whether or not the animal is landed in that place, it is treated as an imported animal and is subject to the normal six months quarantine on its return e.g. a pet taken on a small pleasure boat which ties up at a foreign port or one taken on a day trip to France on a cross-channel ferry.

In March 1975 an Eastbourne couple with their mongrel dog Dollar, were rescued in the English Channel after

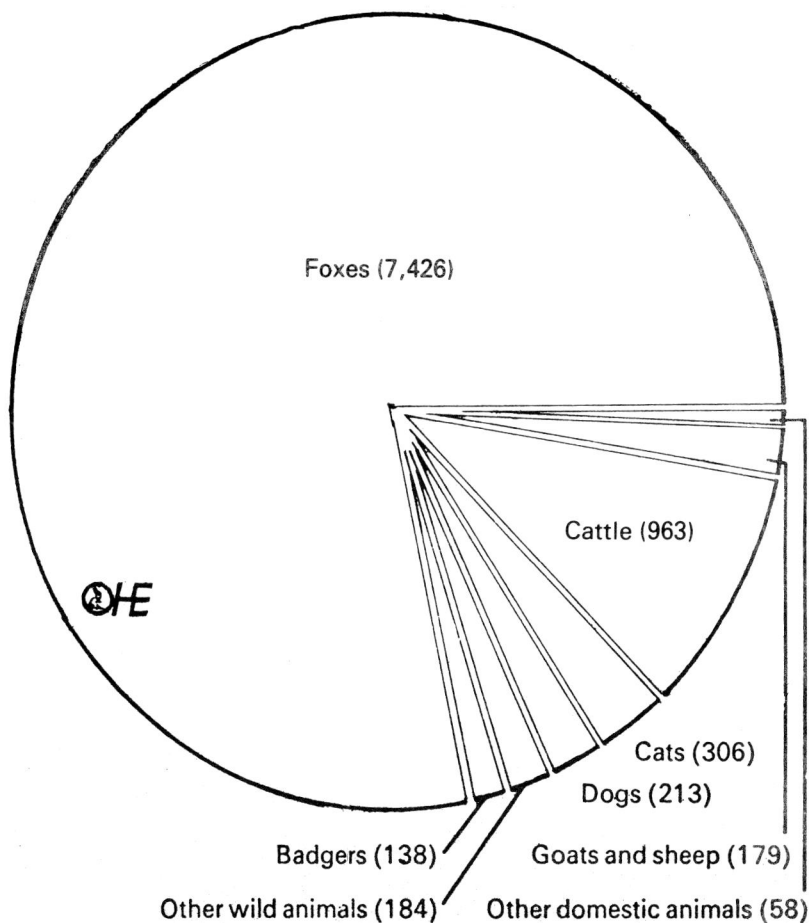

**Figure 4**—*Rabies in France, March 1968 – December 1975 (numbers of confirmed animal cases)*
*Source* Centre d'etudes sur la rage

Foxes (7,426)

Cattle (963)

Cats (306)

Dogs (213)

Badgers (138)

Goats and sheep (179)

Other wild animals (184)

Other domestic animals (58)

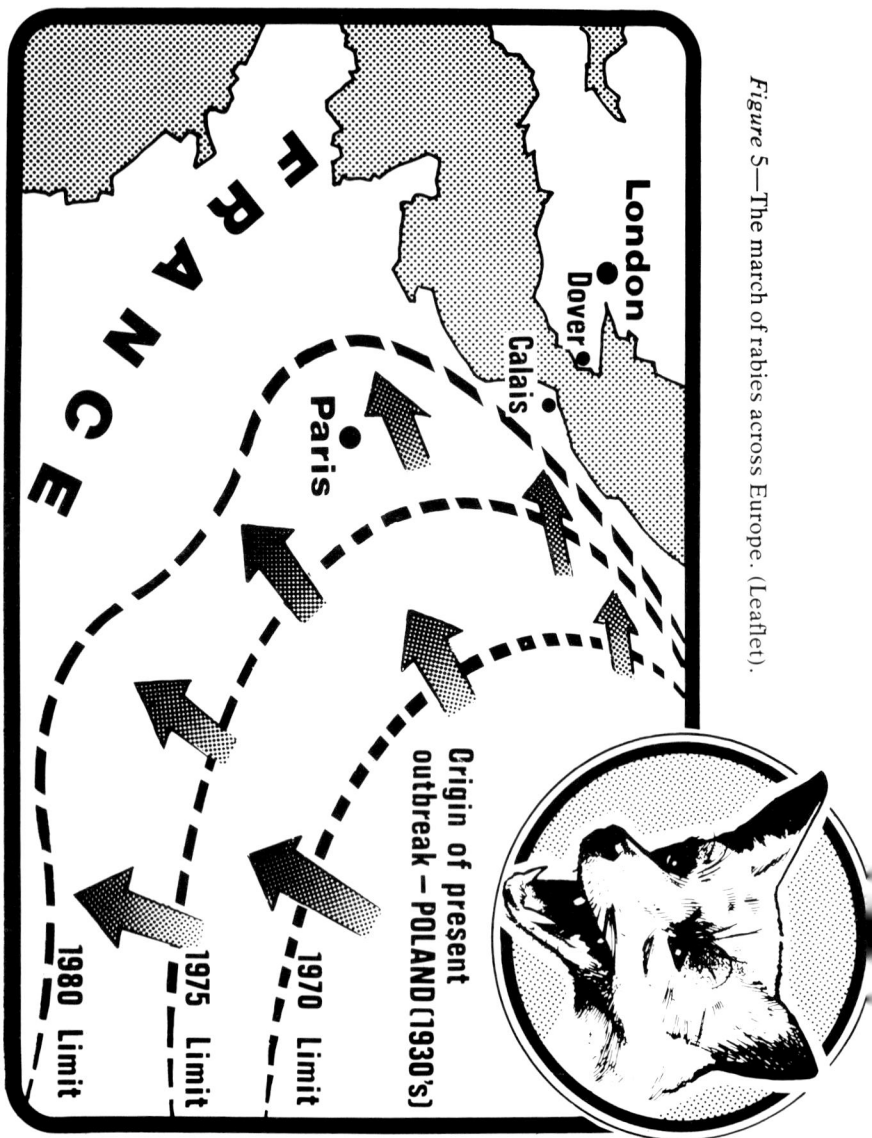

*Figure* 5—The march of rabies across Europe. (Leaflet).

their yacht had run into difficulties in rough weather. The ferry boat Leopard took them aboard on its run to Le Harve and returned later to Southampton. Officials at Southampton came on board with an authorised carrier to take the dog into quarantine kennels. Its owner argued with the officials and said that it had not set foot in France. He jumped over the side on to the quay and made off with the dog which was hidden in various places before finally being tracked down, ''arrested'' and placed in quarantine. The owner was subsequently fined for attempting to evade the importation order.

Under the Order any animal on board a vessel from abroad tied up in British waters must at all times be securely confined within an enclosed part of the vessel from which it cannot escape. It is the master's duty to see that it does not come into contact with any other animal other than one with which it has travelled to Great Britain, and in no circumstances may it land. Should an animal be lost accidently the master must immediately report the fact to a diseases of animals inspector, police constable or Customs and excise officer.

It is not good enough for a ship's master to tie up his dog on deck and he must be made to realize that he is not allowed to take it for a quick walk around the docks.

The summer of 1976 saw the authorities actively engaged in dealing with offences concerning pets on and off vessels. The captain of a Russian super trawler was fined two hundred pounds plus fifty pounds costs for failing to secure a kitten on board while in harbour and for allowing it to land. Officials spotted the crew playing with the animal aboard and later saw them let it loose on the quayside. The Russians have a rule that no pets are allowed on shipping fleet vessels so they broke their own laws as well as ours!

A Dutch yachtsman was fined fifty pounds at Chichester

for entering the harbour with two Siamese cats on board and in Guernsey a similar fine was imposed on a French yachts-man for allowing his Alsatian to run free on deck when his boat was tied up in St. Peter Port harbour. Two Finnish seamen were each fined four hundred pounds for illegally exercising a mongrel on the quayside at Birkenhead while on the Scilly Isles a French trawler crewman pleaded guilty to allowing his black mongrel bitch ashore so that it could urinate. The call of nature cost him four hundred pounds! The Swedish captain of a yacht, charged at Woolwich with allowing his dog to roam free on the deck while it was moored in the Thames, opted for six months in prison rather than pay a six hundred pounds fine.

In two incidents on the Isle of Wight a Frenchman was hustled back on to his boat by yachtsmen at Cowes who saw him land with his pet terrier and a fellow countryman got as far as the shops with his sheep dog, which made a pass at a corgi on the way, before being arrested. Both dogs were quarantined and the offenders subsequently fined a total of seven hundred pounds by the Island court.

Following the 1974 Importation Order the General Council of British Shipping and the mercantile unions jointly agreed that no more pets would be allowed aboard British merchant ships because of the increasing dangers of rabies being brought into the U.K. Sufficient notice was given to allow pets to be humanely disposed of. The move meant that thousands of dogs and cats as well as a number of animals less often considered to be traditional pets e.g. monkeys, lion cubs and even scorpions either had to go ashore in countries that would have them, or be put down. A similar ban was also imposed on the keeping of pets on vessels of the Royal Navy.

*OFFENCES AGAINST THE ORDER*

The Order is, in the main, enforced by county council diseases of animals inspectors but similar powers are given to the police and Ministry veterinary inspectors. Customs Officers, whose surveillance duties form the first line of defence, can also take proceedings under their own legislation.

Where an animal is illegally landed or there is some other contravention of the Order or a licence granted under it, the inspector may, without prejudice to later prosecution proceedings, order the person in charge to re-export it or place it in quarantine at approved premises at his or the owner's expense. If the person in charge refuses to co-operate, the inspector can seize the animal and make the quarantine arrangements himself with the over-riding option of arranging the animal's destruction.

The maximum penalty in a magistrate's court under summary proceedings is at present four hundred pounds, although legislation is proposed, arising from the recommedations of the James Committee on Distribution of Criminal Business, to increase this figure to one thousand pounds. Where deliberate intent to evade the provisions of the Order can be shown, the maximum penalty on indictment is an unlimited fine and/or up to one year's imprisonment.

Before the Order was introduced, early in 1975, it was common practice, except in cases of deliberate smuggling, for illegal landings to be treated as technical offences where prosecution was not considered to be justified. Inspectors usually made arrangements for animals not covered by a licence to be dealt with by service of a notice at the point of entry requiring them to be taken to quarantine by an authorised carrier. At that time the subject of rabies was not taken seriuosly in the U.K. as it has been since and many people, due to lack of publicity, were genuinely unaware of the steps they should have taken.

On the other hand, the paltry fines imposed in cases that came to court, meant that it was thought by some to be worth the risk of smuggling an animal in and avoiding

quarantine fees. Prior to 1975 the average fines had been
fifty pounds while in that year there were fifty two
prosecutions, including one on indictment of two hundred
pounds plus a similar amount in costs and a sentence of
six months suspended for a year. The average fine rose to
one hundred and seventy pounds.

In the first half of 1976, fifty prosecutions were taken
with an average fine of two hundred and sixteen pounds
meted out. In one case two offenders were sentenced to
three months imprisonment in a case of deliberate animal
smuggling. In view of the step up in the number of prosecutions, the Ministry at the time considered that the number of
technical offences were reducing and that a higher proportion of offences deserving prosecution were coming to
light.

The only occasions an animal that had been imported
legally or otherwise can escape spending six months in
quarantine are, when its owner is returning abroad after
a stay in the U.K., or when an animal has been seized by an
inspector following illegal entry, and placed in quarantine,
and the owner subsequently decides to take it home.

An unusual case occurred in late 1976 when a French
woman brought twenty five miniature poodle puppies
from kennels in the U.K. and took them over to France
on the Newhaven — Dieppe ferry. The French authorities refused entry to seventeen because they were
under three months of age. The owner returned to England with the dogs and on arrival at Newhaven, being
without a licence, was charge with importing them illegally. The dogs were taken into quarantine and their owners
subsequently fined three hundred pounds for the offence.
Six weeks later, having paid the fine, and nine hundred pounds in quarantine and veterinary fees, she
collected her dogs which were now old enough to be
imported into France. The animals were taken to the
port by an authorised carrier and seen aboard the ferry

by the local diseases of animals inspector.

The Rabies (Control Order) 1974 which lays down procedures that would be adopted should rabies be discovered outside quarantine in the U.K., will be discussed in a later chapter dealing with emergency arrangements.

## EMBASSIES TO HELP SMUGGLING PROSECUTIONS

In February, 1978 authorities prosecuting under rabies laws had their hands further strengthened when news was received from the Ministry of Agriculture, Fisheries and Food of liason arrangements they had made with Foreign and Commonwealth Offices concerning enquiries alleged to have been made by persons subsequently caught smuggling an animal into the U.K.

In two recent cases owners claimed they had been given wrong advice by British Consulates. In one instance a housewife was given an absolute discharge from a prosecution alleging that she had smuggled her poodle in from Paris. She said she had made enquiries at the British Embassy and local customs office and had been told that all she needed was a vaccination certificate and a railway ticket for the dog which would be taken from her at Dunkirk and placed in quarantine by the British authorities.

Subsequent investigation revealed that no enquiries had been made and what is more the staff at the Embassy had the correct information and were aware of the correct procedure for providing it. All Foreign and Commonwealth offices are geared up to deal with such enquiries and are asked to keep a record of them so that an offender's plea of mitigation can be refuted.

Now that all port and airport staff likely to deal with illegal landings are aware of the position, they will be able to ask detailed questions concerning the consulate at which offenders have made alleged enquiries. They can then refer them quickly to the ministry who will immediately contact the consulate concerned. It will then be easier to decide whether or not to prosecute in the light of a possible plea of mitigation or ignorance of the regulation.

## CUSTOMS RELAXATION POSES NEW RABIES THREAT

As from April 1st, 1978 Customs and Excise introduced new procedures for the control of vessels entering British ports which are claimed by local National Farmers Union branches to represent a severe and alarming threat to our rabies defences.

In the past all vessels from foreign ports were required to fly a yellow flag on entering a port and were automatically boarded by Customs officers. It is now left to ship's masters to radio ahead to the port of entry if there are dogs or other animals on board. In such cases vessels will be boarded but in others only cursory examinations will be made.

Customs claim that by streamlining procedures they will be able to dispense with routine work and devote more attention to vulnerable areas such as yacht and small boat harbours. The new system will allow for misunderstanding by masters of foreign vessels who may care little about the introduction of rabies to England and not want to be deterred from making a quick "turn round".

The Ministry of Agriculture considers that the new selective boarding procedure will permit the formation of mobile teams to operate at peak periods and saturate areas that present the greatest risk of illegal landing of animals.


## RABIES ORDER AMENDED IN 1977

Aimed at tightening anti-rabies import control, an Order which amends the Rabies (Importation of Dogs, Cats and Other Mammals) Order, 1974, came into operation on March 28th, 1977. Its main purposes are to increase the powers of the police in relation to animals in respect of which there are contraventions and to strengthen the control over animals which, although not being landed in Great Britain, are on board a vessel in a British Harbour.

The police have been given similar powers to veterinary

and diseases of animals inspectors for seizing and destroying animals. A police officer will also be able to place an animal in quarantine or arrange for its re-exportation provided the veterinary or diseases of animals inspector agrees.

Dealing with animals aboard vessels in harbour, it now becomes the duty of the person having charge or control of the animal to comply with the order as opposed, in the past, to this being the sole responsibility of the master. An animal is to be at all times restrained and kept securely confined within a totally enclosed part of the vessel from which it cannot escape.

A further additional requirement specifies that no person shall allow the native animal or a native contact animal to go on board a vessel in harbour in Great Britain on which there is an "imported foreign" animal. This does not apply to the use of dogs belonging to the police, H.M. Customs or H.M. Forces so long as such dogs are kept under constant control of a trained handler while on board or the loading on board of any animal or contact animal intended for exportation.

## *AUTHORISED SEA PORTS*

Under an Order which came into effect on March 28th 1977, changes were made in the list of sea ports authorised to receive imports of rabies suspect animals.

Ports which are no longer authorised because their operators have not brought their holding facilities up to the required Standard are :—

Dover (West Dock), Folkestone, London (including Tilbury), Newhaven, and Harwich (Parkeston Quay).

The list of airports at which imports are allowed, remains unchanged.

## Chapter Eight

## RABIES AND SMUGGLING

## *MEANS USED*

It cannot be emphasized too strongly that by far the most likely way that an outbreak of rabies could occur in the U.K. is by the importation of an animal incubating the virus but, at the time, showing no symptoms.

In recent years the illegal import of animals into this country has become easier due to the introduction of the "green channel — nothing to declare" means of clearing customs and to the vast increases in traffic in car and small boat journeys too and from the Continent.

Animals can be smuggled in by various means — by professionals being paid for the job as well as ordinary pet owners, both with no regard for the possible seriousness of the consequences except in cases of certain foreign nationals, who even today, appear to be ignorant of our strict regulations. Animals have been brought in drugged in the backs of cars, in hovercraft, hidden under caravan seats, carried in holdalls and shopping bags and there is even a reported case of an Army officer who went to the lengths of parachuting his dog in.

## *CASE HISTORIES — DOGS AND CATS*

The lengths to which some people will go to avoid being separated from their pets is well illustrated in the case of a married couple who emigrated to South Africa with their crossbred bitch Smokey. A few months later they decided

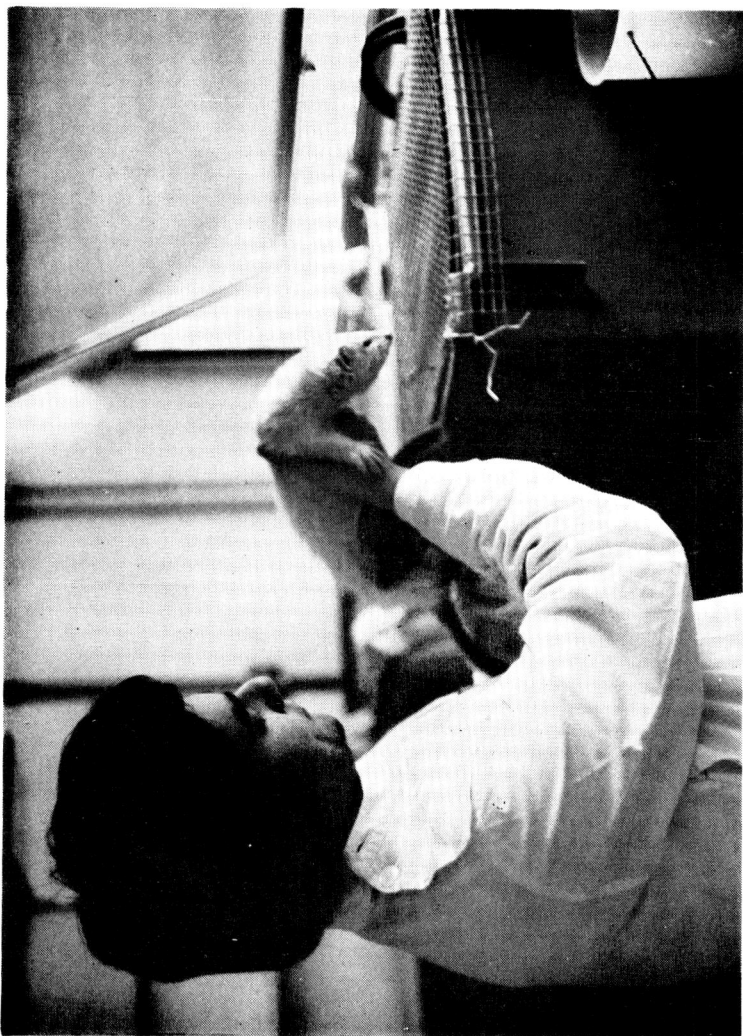

*Plate* 10—A Ferret being used as an artificial host for a study on how fox ticks may be involved in rabies transmission. (*Farmers Weekly photo*).

*Plate* 11—The Animal Quarantine Station at Heathrow Airport showing runways and buildings in the backgroung. (*Photo Corporation of London*).

to return, and to avoid having to place Smokey in quarantine made elaborate plans to deceive the authorities.

They flew from Durban to Amsterdam and there bought a Dutch canal boat before making the dangerous trip across one of the world's busiest shipping lanes in a vessel without safety equipment. They reached Whitstable in Kent after calling at Flushing, Ostend, Dunkirk and Calais. Harbour officials at Whitstable were told that the couple had bought the boat from the Yorkshire Electricity Board in Sheffield and had sailed it from the Trent along the canals to the sea.

The illegal landing came to light when an anonymous complaint was made to Sheffield health officers. Sheffield Crown Court heard the case in January 1976 when the man was given a six months jail sentence suspended for a year and fined two hundred pounds with two hundred pounds costs. The judge said that in his view every reasonable dog lover would condemn the defendant's utterly selfish attitude and wicked anti-social behaviour. The latter, who had no children, said that everything was for the dog — a difficult thing to understand if you are not a dog lover.

Speaking of attitudes, the writer was involved in an incident in the summer of 1974 involving a well educated French woman, when a taxi driver reported having picked her up at Newhaven harbour, and hearing scratching noises coming from one of her bags while on the way to the hotel where she was booked for the night. Accompanied by the Customs Officer on duty at the time and a Newhaven police sergeant I visited the hotel at 3 a.m. where the woman denied having an animal with her. We began a search of the room and when the wardrobe cupboard was opened her cat jumped out. She evaded our questioning despite speaking good English but finally admitted she knew all about our quarantine laws but didn't agree with them. When she was finally convinced that her cat would have to go into quarantine or be put down if she remained in the country, she decided to return with it next day. Meanwhile the animal was seized and detained in a cat box at the harbour over night.

One of the largest fines imposed by a British court for evading import regulations concerned three German holiday makers who brought their boxer dog Simba through Dover in their car. Later police were called to a Chatham hotel where they saw the dog being held on a lead. At Chatham court, the trio, a retired veterinary surgeon, his son and a girl who had accompanied them, were fined one thousand pounds.

Defendants claimed there had been no attempt to hide the dog. They had gone through the green channel with the dog sitting on the front seat. The prosecuting officer agreed there was no intention to smuggle but it was frightening that tourists from the Continent were unaware of British laws and could drive straight through the port. The German Embassy said there were adequate posters in their country warning Germans of our regulations. It was no excuse not to have read them.

At first defendants refused to pay the fine and faced ninety days in prison. Later the son, who had wanted to stage a hunger strike in protest at the treatment they had received said that if he had done so, his father, who was a sick man, would have joined him. He paid the fine plus a seventy pounds bill for quarantining Simba while he attended to business in London in connection with his antique firm in Germany.

Contraventions of the regulations requiring animals to travel in approved containers as freight cargo, have been dealt with in the courts. British Airways were fined four hundred pounds at Uxbridge for allowing a Siamese cat to travel first class in a container from Malta to Heathrow — while its lady owner went second class! The company was charged because it had allowed her to board the aircraft with the animal, contrary to regulations.

A mexican woman, Mrs Maria de Bradley, who smuggled

her Chinese poodle bitch Blackie through Heathrow in a sealed carrier hold-all so that she would not be seen was fined two hundred and fifty pounds for failing to have it carried in a suitable container and the maximum fine of four hundred pounds for evading import regulations.

The case came to light when a suspicious neighbour of her mother-in-law with whom she was staying with her husband and three year old daughter in Brigg, Humberside, reported the presence of the dog which had by now given birth to four pupies, to the local consumer protection department.

The first case involving a prison sentence without suspension, occurred in July 1976 when an English lecturer and an American student were each sentenced to three months imprisonment at Maidstone Crown Court for smuggling two dogs into Britain. The lecturer was also fined two hundred pounds. The couple were the first to be brought before a Crown Court in Kent in a case involving the illegal importation of animals and were charged under article 17 of the Rabies Order 1974 with committing the indictable offence of deliberate smuggling with intent to evade the order.

The dogs were found hidden in a compartment behind the front seats, covered by a blanket and under sedation when they arrived at Dover's "green lane" customs channel. Customs officers, carrying out a routine search made the discovery. The dog belonged to the American woman who had flown from New York to Brussels where her companion had picked her up and drove her in his van to catch a cross-channel ferry. Had she flown direct from Heathrow, the chances of the dogs being discovered were far greater than they were coming by ferry.

When the judge passed sentence he said that smuggling animals was potentially more dangerous than smuggling drugs. It was distressing to have to impose prison sentences, but animal lovers had to realize the great danger to the nation of smuggling their pets into Britain. The holiday season, he said was well under way and many people might be tempted to take their pets abroad and smuggle them back home. The court had to set an example to let animal lovers know the penalties.

The case had two sequels. The lecturer resigned from his post at a Luton College of Further Education and the woman appealed against the sentence. She was told by Lord Justice Roskill that appeal courts would have no hesitation in upholding prison sentences imposed by Crown Courts. Mere sentimental attachments to animals could not possibly be allowed to excuse the quite deliberate infringement of the law which was passed for the greater protection of the inhabitants of this country against a disease from which Britain had so far been free.

Although the American had abandoned her appeal, Lord Roskill said the case should be publicised for the guidance of Crown Courts and magistrates. He did not think it was sufficiently realized that offences committed knowingly and with intent to evade the prohibition of animal imports, were triable on indictment.

In August of the same year a Dutchman and his English girl friend were sentenced to four months imprisonment at Canterbury Crown Court for smuggling an Afghan hound and two cats through Customs checks at Dover. The couple moved to England from Holland in January and gave the animals a mild sedative before placing them on the back seat of the car and covering them with a travel rug.

Police were informed after the couple arrived at the girl's home in East Hardwick, Yorkshire and the animals were brought from their hiding place. Before they could be taken into quarantine the dog, still in a dazed condition, ran off into the village. After its capture all three animals were taken to approved premises and later released, after being cleared of infection.

The Guernsey Board of Administration takes an even

more serious view of rabies than does the British Government. Any animal illegally imported there is automatically destroyed. A native woman fined seven hundred pounds for importing a half starved stray from Morocco appealed unsuccessfully against the decision that the dog should be put down. In a press release the Board stated that in no circumstances would it be prepared to expose the Island to the possible introduction of the dreadful disease of rabies from which there is no cure.

## CASE HISTORIES IN OTHER PETS

Although by far the greatest number of detected cases of animal smuggling involve dogs and cats, the authorities and the courts have recently dealt with a variety of other illegal pet importations. In 1974 a London businessman brought two monkeys through Gatwick airport in a bag. The offence would probably have gone undetected but for the fact that he was bitten by one of the animals which later died. Fearing he might have contracted rabies he went to his doctor and took the second monkey to a veterinary surgeon. The latter reported the matter, leading to the monkey's owner appearing in court and being fined two hundred pounds.

An eagle-eyed traffic warden in Hastings interrupted a two hundred and sixty thousand miles round-the-world journey for and Australian couple and their pet marmoset monkey Peppercorn. The warden saw the monkey peeping through the window of its owner's caravanette which carried an Australian registration number. The man was fined the maximum of four hundred pounds and the nine and a half year journey which had so far taken the couple and their monkey to sixty seven countries was temporaraily halted while they cabled home for money to meet the cost of Peppercorn's stay in quarantine.

More fortunate, particularly as his work involved him in tropical diseases, was a Polish professor who received a one year's conditional discharge for illegally importing a monkey. Spotted playing in a car in Kensington, it was said to have been vaccinated against rabies in Zaire, and to be no risk to anybody in Britain. It was later "deported" when the professor and his family left the country.

A French tourist was fined two hundred and fifty pounds at Plymouth for bringing his family's pet guinea pig into the country illegally. Defendant said they had brought their pet with them because they loved him and could not bear to be parted. The animal spent fifteen days in quarantine to ensure he was not incubating rabies. Had this occurred a massive operation would have been launched in London, Oxford, Porlock, Newquay, Tintagel and St.Ives where the man, his wife and two daughters had stayed on a camping holiday.

Young teenage boys are prone to fancying mice as pets. Two were tempted and found themselves in trouble for bringing them home from France. A twelve year old Kettering boy on an exchange visit with a family in Paris was given their pet white mouse and brought it through Customs at Dover in a cardboard box on top of his luggage. When the offence was discovered, the animal was seized by Ministry of Agricultural officials and destroyed. After considering a prosecution, the Northamptonshire County Council who had taken the case over decided instead to give the boy a caution. When he knew the mouse could be harbouring rabies, he said he was afraid of it.

A twelve year old American boy aboard a ferry travelling from Dieppe to Newhaven was discovered by one of the crew to have a white mouse in his luggage. The discovery was radioed to Newhaven Harbour prior to the boat docking and the boy and his pet detained on board. The diseases of animals inspector told the lad that the mouse could go back to France, be put into quarantine or be destroyed. An animal loving member of the ship's crew overheard the boy's dilemma and said he would take the animal back to a family in Dieppe who would give it a home.

Also to be considered, although the chances of a case happening are fairly remote, is the accidental entry of an animal with or incubating rabies. Possibly the most likely way that this could occur is by an animal accidently being shut in one of the giant containers in the cross channel "roll-on roll-off" ferries or those transported in purpose built container ships, while being loaded.

In July 1977, a 14 year old Belgian girl staying with an English family in Hastings was fined £50 at Hastings juvenile court for illegally importing a hamster into the country.

It was eight days before her host, who was thanked by the chairman of the court for her public spirited action in reporting the matter, found the hamster in her bedroom.

The girl said she could not bear to be parted from her pet and had no idea she was breaking the law. If she had left it at home it would have died as both her parents were away. She put the animal in a tin box after making holes in the top before she left Belgium and when she arrived in Hastings hid it in a wardrobe and let it out twice a day.

A year later in the same court a 14 year old German girl who knew the law about importing animals and who had been worried by warning notices she saw at the port and on the ferry, still persisted in bringing her white rabbit through Dover without declaring it when on a visit to this country as a student.

She told her hosts that it was a present for their children. The latter's parents put the rabbit in a hamster cage and, knowing the law intended to report the matter to the authorities. But the authorities in the shape of the local diseases of animals inspector Stan Tomlin who lived near by, heard about the rabbit first, seized it and had it destroyed.

Its owner who was fined £40 with £10 costs, was told by the chairman of the juvenile court concerned that had she been an adult she could have been fined £400 for the offence.

## ACCIDENTAL ENTRIES

What started out as a good turn to please a nine year old girl suffering from spina bifida, ended in her mother being fined three hundred pounds by Wycombe magistrates court in March 1977 for smuggling a pet hamster into the country.

The family spent the previous Christmas in Belgium and the girl's uncle bought her the hamster which was brought home in a tin and not declared when the family went through the customs. The girl was so pleased with her new acquisition that she told nurses about it when she went into hospital. The staff contacted the authorities resulting in the mother's appearance in court.

Although the hamster was found to be rabies free it was destroyed at the family's request.

The fine imposed was the maximum for a juvenile offence.

In November 1976 a sealed container originating from Turkey, was opened in a cold store in Peterborough when two cats were discovered. That the animals had remained alive in a temperature of minus eighteen degrees for sixteen days was remarkable but they were quarantined for some ten days just in case they were developing rabies.

An earlier case in which the writer was involved concerned a Spanish lorry laden with tomatoes which had been pulled into Newhaven port's freight shed for examination by Customs officials. The rear doors of the vehicle were opened so that trays of tomatoes could be brought out for weighing and inspection when a cat was seen charging about among the cargo. The doors were quickly closed and I was telephoned as the duty diseases of animals inspector. The divisional veterinary officer was contacted and said the animal must be seized before the lorry left the port — he would not allow this to be done when the lorry was unloaded at its destination. Two British rail porters climbed into the

*Plate* 12—The Surgery at the Animal Quarantine Station, Heathrow
Airport.                                   (*Photo Corporation of London*).

*Figure* 6—La Rage. Central Office of Information Poster 1976.

eighteen inch space at the top of the lorry in an attempt
to catch the cat which ran to the front of the forty feet long
vehicle and trapped itself low down near the refrigeration
unit.

By this time the next boat carrying more lorries to deal
with was due, and to avoid holding up port operations,
attempts at capture were abandoned until the following
morning. Then, with the freight shed doors closed, two
doors in the side of the lorry were opened and men began
unloading the cargo to clear a space to search from. Eventually the cat was seen again beside the refrigeration
unit and reports from inside the lorry suggested that it
looked in poor shape and might even be dead.

Without warning it darted across the top of the tomato
trays and sprang out of the back of the lorry, hurling itself
against the shed door in an attempt to escape. Finally
it was cornered by the lorry driver and seized by a harbour
policeman who was wearing gloves. The cat which, considering it had been closed in the lorry for five days without
food and water, was remarkably active and agile, bit the
policeman through his gloves before being bundled into a
ventilated box.

Because of the possibility of it being rabid and, due to
its five day incarceration in a confined refrigerated space,
it was, naturally, extremely wild, the port health inspector,
who had been called in to see if the tomatoes had been
contaminated, immediately arranged for anti-rabies serum
to be sent by rail from Colindale laboratory so that the
policeman's doctor could give him the series of fourteen
injections. When Colindale asked for the cat to be quarantined so that, if in good health at the end of five days, the
treatment of the policeman could be ended, an order
previously given to a local veterinary surgeon to put the
animal down, was cancelled.

The cat went into quarantine and after five days showed
no signs of the disease. After being put down its head

was sent to the Ministry laboratory for rabies tests. It was decided to complete the course of injections on the policeman who had to be off duty for a while with side effects. As the cat had no owner, the cost of transporting it to quarantine, its short stay there and final disposal was met by the administering authority — the County Council. The policeman's mishap was treated as an industrial injury and the expenses involved were probably met by his employers.

A further instance of how a rabid animal could be introduced accidentally, occurred in June 1978 when the driver of a container lorry originating from Le Cloud in France, spotted a cat under the tarpaulin when he was checking his load in a Bexhill car park. The container, packed with 680 packages of furniture, which was on its way to Huddersfield, had been parked for five days in Newhaven harbour prior to being picked up by the driver.

The driver alerted the police who in turn contacted the duty diseases of animals inspector Hector Chamberlain. The lorry was driven to Bexhill fire station, the only building in the town large enough to take it. All fire appliances were removed and the doors of the building closed.

As the tarpaulin was rolled back, the cat jumped out, tore round the fire station and leapt at windows in an attempt to get away. Mr Chamberlain caught the animal which bit him through his protective gloves before being put down by a veterinary surgeon who had been called in to deal with the emergency. A later examination proved that the animal was not carrying rabies.

The authorities had nothing but praise for the driver whose prompt action resulted in the animal being confined and disposed of with no danger of it escaping and causing a 12 mile radius quarantine to be imposed.

Rabies could be introduced by an affected rodent gaining shore from a boat. In one incident an alert was set off when a yacht from Spain declared a wild rat aboard when it arrived at Penzance. The Cornish harbour authorities ordered it to leave and it made its way to Southampton where police asked Coastguards to issue sighting reports so that quarantine arrangements could be made.

## SURVEILLANCE

Surveillance at ports and airports is in the hands of Customs and Excise officers. However, they have a wide range of duties and the detection of the smuggling of dutiable goods is their main priority. Even this work has to be carried out on a "spot check" basis except where suspicions are aroused, to save massive build up of traffic during peak holiday periods. Due to the publicity campaign launched by the Government in the summer of 1976, all air port and sea port staffs are well aware of the risks attached to animal smuggling and police, dock staffs and members of crews act as voluntary watch-dogs.

There is a greater risk of an animal being landed at one of the many points along the coast where yachts can berth. Although Customs officers board such vessels and explain the law to those carrying pets, it would be unrealistic to expect constant surveillance to be achieved.

*Chapter Nine*

## RABIES AND PUBLICITY

Ways media is used — reactions to publicity — stunt that misfired.

### WAYS MEDIA IS USED

Up until May 1976 when the Ministry of Agriculture launched a Fifty thousand pounds publicity canpaign, "The Rabies Awareness Campaign 1976", the British public were, generally speaking, ill-informed of the risks attaching to a possible outbreak of rabies. We are an island and have been free from the disease for over fifty years. Few people here have had experience of it and its horrors. It's approach to the northern coast of France however, prompted the Government to alert the country to the consequences of illegally importing an animal harbouring the disease.

The Ministry up-dated their posters which were exhibited at ports, airports, marinas and yacht clubs. New, colourful leaflets were prepared and distributed through local authorities, travel agents and, with the help of the British Embassies, to suitable sporting and yachting organisations in most European countries and elsewhere in the world. Among European countries covered were France, Belgium, Holland, Germany, Italy, Spain and Portugal.

County Councils as diseases of animals authorities augmented Ministry publicity in a number of cases by producing their own posters and leaflets. East Sussex County Council, for example, produced two posters in varying sizes — one, "To Travel Your Pet Needs a Passport" and the other, in French, German, Spanish, Italian and Dutch — "Rabies Kills in any Language". The former was designed for display in libraries, police stations, pet

*88*

shops and travel agancies, while the latter was used at ports and yacht marinas.

The Animal Welfare Trust produced a six-page pamplet with a picture of a rabid dog on the front captioned "A Smuggled Dog Can Kill a Child". The pamphlet briefly described rabies and its symptoms, penalties for pet smuggling and what would happen if the disease came to Britain. The import regulations are set out in German, French, Spanish and Italian and names and addresses of some of the authorised carrying agents and quarantine establishments are listed, together with the authorised entry points and addresses where import licences can be obtained.

Publicity perhaps made its greatest impact through the mass media of press, radio and television. It was hardly possible to open a newspaper, national or local, during the summer of 1976 without reading some reference to rabies. The disease has a kind of science fiction-like, macabre fascination and makes a good subject for articles and press reports. As well as general interest articles, drawing attention to the dangers and possible flaws in our defence plans, further momentum was given to the campaign by the deaths in humans that occurred in Britain, and the increased penalties imposed, including imprisonment, for animal smuggling cases brought to light.

Radio too played its part. Rabies was introduced into serials in woman's programmes and Ministry veterinary officers, Customs officials and officers of diseases of animals authorities spoke on the subject on local radio programmes. Rabies figured as well in drama on radio. A James Follett play — The Rabid Summer — told what happened when rabies broke out during August in a small seaside town. A critic wrote that it was a gripping play with several scenes offering the kind of vivid reality only possible through radio. No television play for instance could have shown a succession of school children being bitten hard by a rabid dog in the playground. It would, he said, be no bad thing if this play were to be repeated once a month indefinitely.

A number of T.V. programmes were devoted to rabies and here it is possible to bring the horrors of the disease visually into the viewers lives. In a B.B.C. programme in May, Mad Dogs and Smugglers, Chris Brasher's presentation managed to avoid sensationalism and scaremongering without for one moment letting his audience lose sight of the seriousness of the disease. There were disturbing examples of young victims and poignant interviews with relatives of persons who had died from rabies. The latter made conversations with selfish sentimental pet owners found guilty of smuggling offences, especially hard to tolerate. The programme made it clear that Customs Officers at ports of entry cannot be expected to take the responsibility of keeping the disease out of Britain on their own. The nation was called on to help and be watchful.

The Ministry have available a particularly harrowing French film "La Rage" and this has been shown with telling effect to officials and members of County Council public protection committees who had to consider justifying expenditure on publicity and defence plans.

A more subtle form of publicity whose introduction happened to coincide with the Ministry campaign, was the production by the Islands of Trinidad and Tobago of two special thirty-cent stamps to honour one of their citizens who was responsible for the advance in the battle against the disease in the tropics.

The stamps depict the work of Dr Lennox Pawan who established in 1932 that rabies was transmitted by the vampire bat. He isolated the virus and prepared a serum and is included on the roll of honour at the Pasteur Institute in Paris where he worked. One of the stamps shows a vampire bat and the other carries a portrait of Dr Pawan who died in 1957.

Articles and leaders on rabies appeared in magazines, journals and house journals read by persons whose work could bring them into contact with the disease, e.g. Environmental Health, and Portcullis, the offical staff newspaper of H.M. Customs and Excise. The students of Sussex University were reached when a local diseases of animals inspector contributed a piece — "Rabies Kills" — for their campus news sheet. The same officer organised exhibitions of posters, leaflets and relevant literature in branch libraries in his area.

It is often said with truth that we make fun of things we do not fully understand or are afraid of. And so rabies has been given publicity, perhaps unwittingly, by humour in the shape of cartoons, unintentional newspaper "funnies" and shaggy-dog stories.

A West country newspaper reported a spokesman as saying that in his fight to keep out rabies he was calling for the death sentence for smuggled animals and stiffer penalties for their owners!

Then there was the cartoon showing two dogs sitting outside one of H.M. Prisons and one saying to the other "The question is, how do we smuggle *them* out?", and the one of the rather ill informed local government officer who, on reading a poster on the notice board — Keep Rabies Out of Britain — was heard to mutter "I couldn't agree more. Even if they have got British passports!"

The French who have to accept rabies as part of their every day life set off a scare in this country in August 1976 when customs officers heard a French radio programme telling all France how to beat the British anti-rabies laws and smuggle their dogs into the U.K.

Urgent messages passed from Customs H.Q. in the City of London to the Ministry of Agriculture and Fisheries in Whitehall. As a result all Customs officers were put on full alert at sea and airports in case French listeners tried the methods recommended by the radio. The British Embassy in Paris was asked to check on the programme and, if necessary, protest at its contents. This proved unnecessary as it transpired that the programme put out by the France Inter Station was satirical — to the embarrassment of our own Ministry. The Foreign Office said it was a misunderstanding and only someone not able to speak native French would have taken it seriously. The programme was a joke — a play on words which the French would take that way but which a Briton might mistake for the real thing. The Chairman of the Customs and Excise Board said that he *had* sent out a circular to his staff telling them to make sure that nothing in the programme could breach our security, when one of his staff had reported hearing the broadcast.

The situation resolved itself when the programme director told the Paris Embassy staff that the broadcast was a bit of fun. The Customs Chief, when asked about the law-beating suggestions made over the radio, replied that it would obviously not be helpful to suggest ways of evading the law!

An M.P. reacted strongly to an advertisement relating to the liner Queen Elizabeth II. Michael Jopling, Tory spokesman on Agriculture, was horrified when he saw a large display in a Sunday newspaper inviting Q.E.II passengers to a shopping spree to purchase duty free wines, spirits and tobacco, jewellery and Yves St Laurent evening dresses at the Boat Deck Arcade. The offending part of the advertisement was a picture in the bottom left hand corner of a lady clutching armfuls of shopping with a dog on a lead trotting along in front.

Mr Jopling said that the obvious implication was that passengers could walk their pets around the boat. We couldn't afford this sort of carelessness, he said, with rabies only just across the Channel. The advertisement could be misunderstood particularly if it was shown on the other side of the Atlantic. He could visualise someone bringing a dog on board, finding out he shouldn't have it and trying to hide it in a carrier bag. Cunard, the owners of

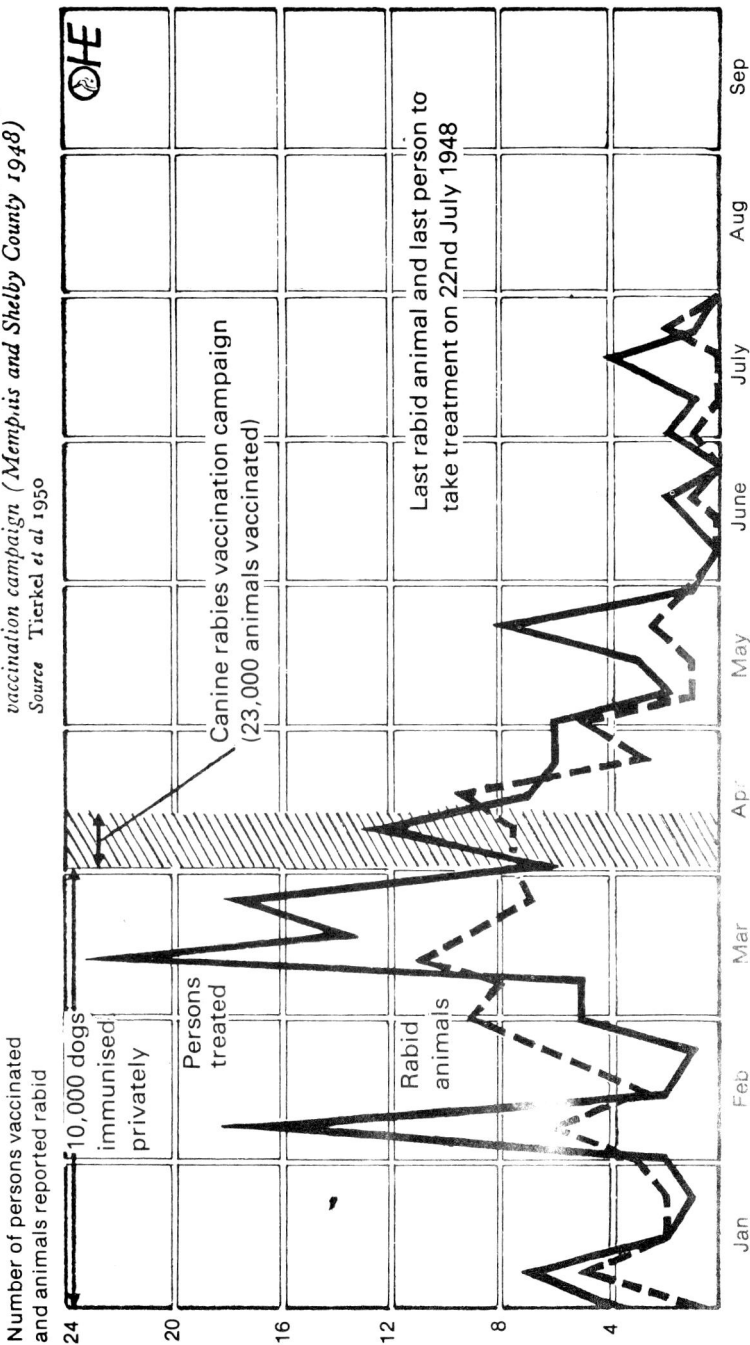

Figure 7—*Effect on human uptake of rabies prophylaxis of a canine vaccination campaign (Memphis and Shelby County 1948)*
Source Tierkel et al 1950

Number of persons vaccinated
and animals reported rabid

24

20

16

12

8

4

Jan    Feb    Mar    Apr    May    June    July    Aug    Sep

10,000 dogs immunised privately

Persons treated

Canine rabies vaccination campaign (23,000 animals vaccinated)

Rabid animals

Last rabid animal and last person to take treatment on 22nd July 1948

OHE

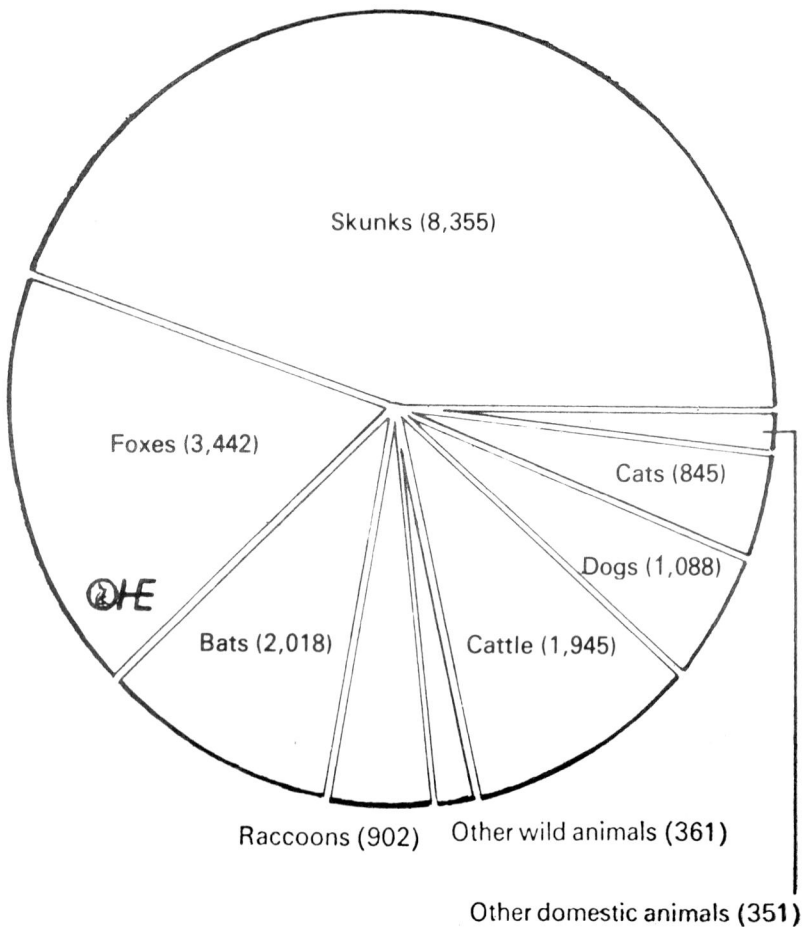

**Figure 8**—*Rabies in the United States 1969–73 (number of confirmed animal cases)*
*Source* Centre for Disease Control

Skunks (8,355)

Foxes (3,442)

Cats (845)

Dogs (1,088)

Bats (2,018)

Cattle (1,945)

Raccoons (902)     Other wild animals (361)

Other domestic animals (351)

Q.E.II, changed the display to show the woman without her dog.

## REACTIONS TO PUBLICITY

Reaction to the Government's publicity campaign was favourable in the main. There was a ready willingness to co-operate in displaying posters. People wanted to talk about rabies and find out more about it. Ministry veterinary departments, the police and diseases of animals inspectors were kept busy dealing with reports from the public of strange behaviour among wild animals such as foxes and squirrels. Dogs and cats spotted in vehicles with foreign registration numbers and Continental lorries were notified to the authorities and animals taken ill with rabies-like symptoms were treated as though they had the disease until the contrary was established.

The campaign was used to stir up the feeling against the dog by those who were calling for action to stop him fouling public places. The threat of rabies was another weapon in their armoury, and reinforced the arguments that licence fees should be increased, strays dealt with and the dog banned from parks and recreation grounds.

There were those who thought the campaign had gone too far. The R.S.P.C.A. took this line after receiving calls from worried members of the public. A member of its governing council condemned the publicity as scare-mongering alleging it to be a terror campaign with a deliberate use of fear designed so that in the event of a confirmed rabies case in this country, the Goverment would be able to proceed with its drastic measures with the suitably anaes-thetised public looking the other way. The last thing they wanted was people abandoning their pets because of irrational fears. There were better ways than frightening people into a belief that the disease was some sort of Black Plage racing across Europe and about to leap the Channel and wipe us all out.

During the summer of 1976 police in several Southern counties followed up a number of reports of dogs seen in foreign cars. In two cases owners were able to prove they had bought the animals in the U.K. Sussex police seized a monrel dog from the cab of a Spanish container lorry after information that the vehicle had docked at Newhaven earlier, was carrying a dog. When he was stopped at Uckfield, the driver told police that the dog had jumped into his cab when he stopped just north of Newhaven. He had intended taking it to London and dumping it there. When his story was confirmed by the drivers of four other lorries, stopped at Uckfield during the search for the dog, he was allowed to continue his journey to Covent Garden with a load of fruit. The dog was taken into police custody as a stray to await being claimed by its owner.

A fifteen-year old Norfolk boy was commended by Great Yarmouth magistrates for reporting the master of a Cypriot motor vessel whose dog ran off his boat which was moored at a quay. The boy's dog chased the master's animal back to the ship resulting in a four hundred pounds fine for not keeping it securely confined within the vessel.

Because one of their gang was scratched by the ship's cat while unloading cars from an Irish vessel, the Dundalk, fifty dockers at Harwich stopped work for an hour and walked off the ship. The rabies scare was ended when the animal was caught and the port medical authorities informed.

An incident involving an Alsatian dog that had wandered into a south coast restaurant and bitten four people, served as a useful exercise in carrying out the routine to be adopted should the real thing happen. The police had seized the dog and taken it to their kennels after learning from a tag on its collar that its name was Sam and that it purported to come from an address in Palma de Mallorca. The police were advised to inform the divisional community physician. I made sure that the four people who had been bitten had contacted a doctor who decided, as there were no skin abrasions, to wait for an examination of the animal by a veterinary officer, before starting innoculations.

During the night, the dog's owner reported its loss to the police and was able to satisfy them that it had been released from quarantine a month earlier. The animal was examined and later released to its mistress.

## STUNT THAT MISFIRED

Towards the end of May 1976 a Sussex local newspaper received a cryptic message from St Remy de Provence in France. Headed "Criticat on Rabies", the message read :—
Watch out for water walkers. E.T.A. Newhaven 12.15 hrs 1.6.76 "Pass a Paw" in paw issued Aggers Minimising risk, "C", Silly to get Rabies 'cos its all the Rage in France. Meet him with Putative Queen of Calvados and consort in Volvo TE164 TMHZM Charnwood Productions out 'of quarantine after Rabies treatment. Pasteur Clinic Marseilles. Wish someone else had been there. Aggers. Ring a Ring O' Rabies, Our tums are jabbed like Hades, Lick, Lick, the Pets are sick, All Die Down.

The message was passed to the county council who alerted police and customs. The car towing a caravan and complete with man, woman and one cat, came on an earlier boat than indicated on the message. An authorised carrier went on board with his van and the cat, which had previously been licensed by the Ministry, was transferred from the car and taken to quarantine. After being closely questioned by Customs men, the cat's owner was told he could leave but asked if he could stay in the port area until 12.15 as he had contacted newspapers radio and T.V. with a view to a publicity exercise. He was told to go but returned later to a shed outside the confines of the port where the only interest in his story came from a local radio station reporter.

He told me that he and his wife were opera singers/journalists and had been living in their caravan in a cave in

95

France. They had both been attacked by a cat and had found great difficulty in obtaining anti-rabies treatment. They were critical of the French authorities for not allowing them to complete the course of injections which lasted four months, in the U.K. The cat they brought with them was a stray picked up in the area where they were living, and for which they had difficulty in finding out the procedure to go through, and eventually obtaining an import licence.

*RABIES REMINDER*

Now that district councils are responsible for dealing with dog licence reminders, one such council — Surrey Heath — is using the document for anti rabies publicity. Just before Christmas each year dog owners in the area, which significantly includes Camberley, receive postcard reminders and alongside the address is written the following message :— "Legislation now imposes heavy fines and possible imprisonment for the smuggling of animals into the country from abroad. This also applies to animals taken abroad even for a few hours. Rabies is a killer disease of humans and animals. In your own interests, please assist in keeping rabies out of the country".

One of the houses to receive a postcard reminder was that of Mr J. E. Nunn, Assistant Secretary at the Ministry of Agriculture and the man responsible for co-ordination of rabies precautions. Mr Nunn wrote to the Association of District Councils commenting that it seemed an excellent way of reaching at least the "legal" dog owners of the country and suggesting that other councils might like to follow suit. The Association was happy to pass the suggestion on its monthly journal — District Councils' Review.

*"SEE HIM OFF RABIES !"*

A local newspaper columnist has thought up a good tip for stopping the anti-social fouling of pavements by dogs.

## Rabies and Publicity

Rename your pet "Rabies" he suggested and when you see a dog about to answer the call of nature send your dog towards it. Then with a stentorian shout, call its name. With any luck the erring owner and dog will take to their heels in fright before any damage has been done.

*Chapter Ten*

# RABIES AND EMERGENCY MEASURES

Control measures — controls on the Continent — controls elswhere — World
Health Organisation's views on controls.

## CONTROL MEASURES

The World Health Expert Committee on Rabies when
referring to organization in infected areas, said that control
programmes are usually most efficiently operated by a
central authority "under a public health officer preferably
a veterinarian". This official should organize the control
measures, ensure full co-ordination between the various
medical and veterinary associations involved and establish
close liaison with animal protection and welfare societies
and other interests. Depending on circumstances, he should
assume responsibility for all local, national, and, where
appropriate, international aspects of the situation.

He should also co-ordinate the diagnosis of rabies,
collection and dispatch of specimens, the setting up of
associated training courses and research projects and the
design of a publicity programme.

When dealing with the control of animals, the Expert
Committee defined the objective as being "the control and
eventual elimination of the disease from reservoir and
vector populations in nature. Practical success depends on
the carrying out of carefully planned programmes using
effective vaccines and control procedures for the common
vector species".

In an area where the disease is established, prophylactic
vaccination of dogs is one of the most important weapons in

rabies control. In newly infected areas, the institution of vaccination programmes for dogs and cats should be accompanied by leashing and confinement of the animal for thirty days to enable immunity to be developed. Stray animals should be collected by trained and equipped personnel and impounded for destruction. The Expert Committee strongly advised that non-vaccinated dogs, cats and other domestic pets bitten by a known rabid animal should be immediately destroyed.

## CONTROLS ON THE CONTINENT

In the Federal Republic of Germany, where rabies is widespread in wild life, when a case is suspected in a previously uninfected area, a public announcement is made and a "danger area" declared. Where rabies is suspected in a dog or cat that has been at large while possibly infective, the size of the restricted area is decided on the basis of local conditions and, where the disease is suspected in wild life, restrictions may be over an area with a radius of ten kilometres. Warning notices are displayed at exits and entrances to the area and such places as railway stations; air and sea ports.

Within such an area dogs must be leashed and cats kept under strict control. Dogs and cats may be taken out of the area only with special permission and after veterinary examination. During their absence they must be restricted in the same way as they would have been within the infected area. Dogs and cats found wandering in the area are either shot or, if possible, caught and detained by authorised persons. Dogs and cats bitten by a rabid animal are destroyed. Horses and cattle suspected of being bitten are isolated and kept under observation for six months (pigs, sheep and goats for three months). During the observation periods animals may only be moved, apart from out to pasture, with special permission and will remain restricted and under veterinary supervision for the full period applicable to the restricted area.

Should an animal be slaughtered, die or be moved, all premises and objects with which it has had contact are immediately disinfected and articles such as collars, badges and muzzles are burnt or destroyed.

An isolated outbreak is considered to have ended and restrictions are lifted if there has been no further case within the area for a period of three months.

In France the Prefect of any area where an isolated outbreak occurs has existing powers to apply restrictions to domestic animals such as leashing, movement control and compulsory vaccination.

Denmark achieved complete success with control measures imposed when rabies crossed her borders with Germany in 1964. Compulsory immunisation of dogs and cats, the restriction of their movements outside controlled areas and the gassing of foxes brought about eradication of the disease in Denmark by 1970. To put the success in its proper perspective, however, it must be remembered that the country has only a narrow land frontier to deal with and did not, in 1964 have to face well established endemic rabies in its wild life. Experience on Continental mainlands under such conditions is less encouraging. For instance in North America and Western Europe generally — both have faced major rabies outbreaks recently — where considerable resources were used for its control, it has not been found possible to contain it.

Rabies was reported as approaching Holland from both West Germany and Belgium in 1967 but intensification of preventive measures such as dog vaccination, the hunting of foxes and the destruction of stray dogs and cats appears to have prevented its introduction.

A case of a dog illegally imported into Holland in 1962 that developed rabies, resulted in the deaths of five people and eight animals and led to an Act which enabled infected animals to be detained or destroyed on suspicion of having

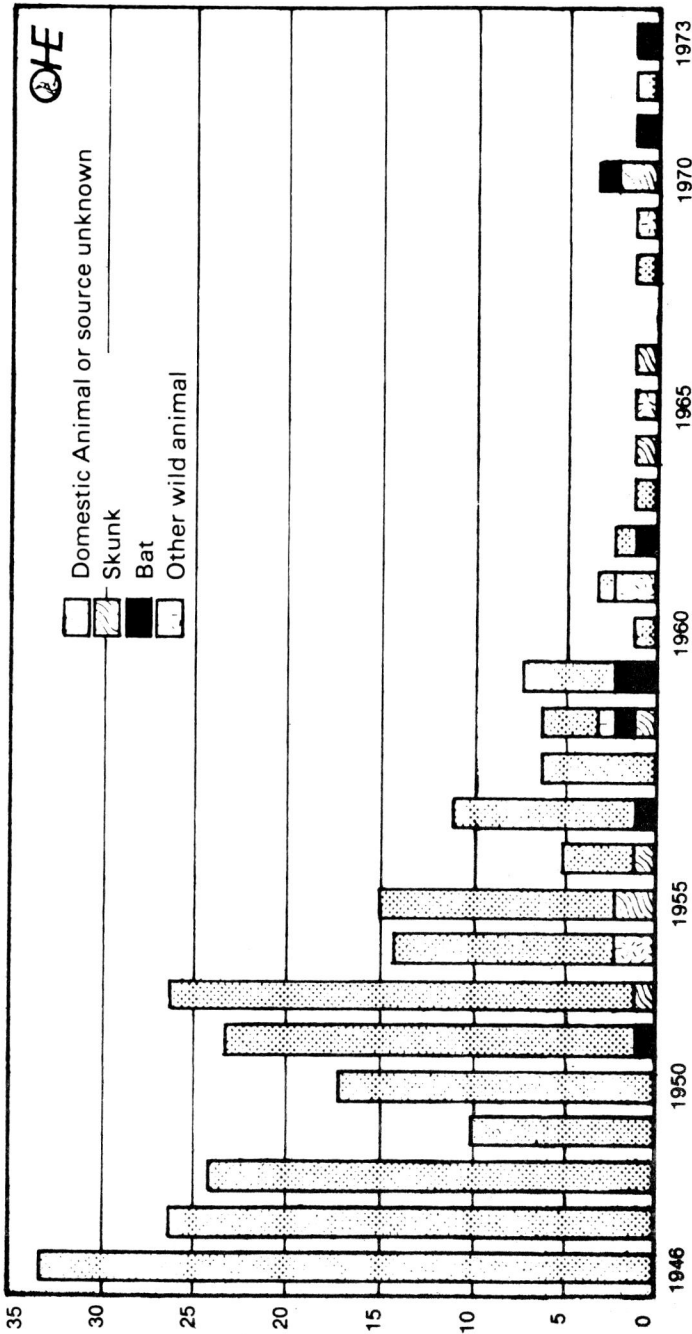

*Figure* 9—Human rabies in the U.S.A. by species of vector, *1946–73*
*Source* Hattwick and Gregg 1975

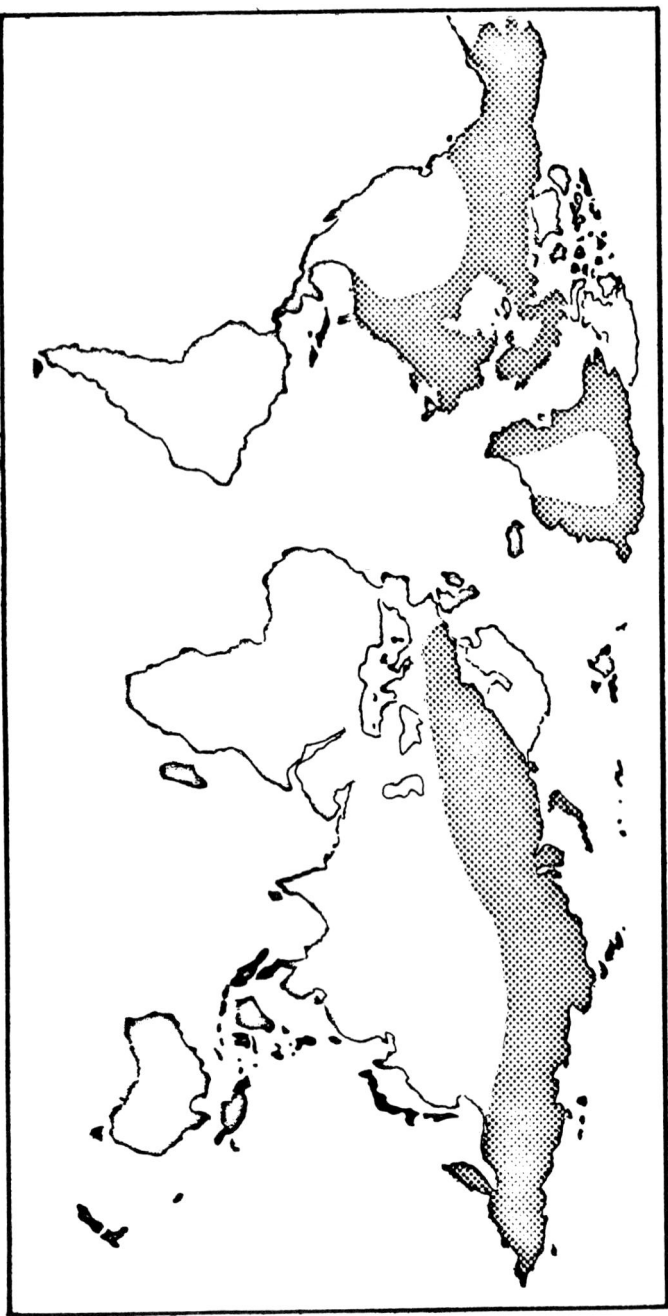

Figure 10— *World distribution of enzootic fox rabies*

Source   Winkler 1975

been infected. The Act also authorised the use of muzzle and leashing restrictions on dogs and prophylactic vaccination of both dogs and cats. Instructions about the action to be taken if a case of rabies occurred were sent to all doctors and veterinary surgeons in the Netherlands.

The 1962 incidents led to the introduction of a Rabies Decree which specifically required at that time the vaccination of all dogs, muzzling and leashing restrictions for all domestic dogs and cats, a prohibition on all assemblies of dogs and cats for show, markets or any other purpose and the destruction of stray animals over the whole country.

In the Netherlands, the department of Health and Agriculture work closely together when dealing with infections and contagious diseases transmissible from animals to man. Each administrative area has a veterinary public health officer who complements the work of his colleague, the counterpart of the British District Community Physician.

## CONTROLS ELSEWHERE

Mass vaccination of dogs and the destruction of strays carried out in Malaya resulted in the eradication of rabies in some eighteen months. Following the war with the Japanese, the disease gained a foothold in the north and spread to the capital Kuala Lumpur where there had been no cases for twenty years.

The public supported a compulsory vaccination programme which together with the destruction of thousands of strays, resulted in a reduction in the number of cases from thirty five to nil in six months.

The veterinary department widened its vaccination campaign to all affected States and later to the whole of the Federation when one hundred and fifteen thousand dogs were vaccinated and thirty thousand destroyed. For the first time in living memory all rabies restrictions were lifted. There was free movement of dogs within the Federation and regulations were amended to allow dogs to enter the country.

Mass vaccination and control of strays in the U.S.A. have also demonstrated the success that can be achieved by these methods in controlling rabies in dogs. In 1946 with a dog population of some 12 million, there were over eight thousand confirmed cases while in 1965 when the numbers had risen to nearly twenty three million, there were only four hundred and twelve cases which further reduced five years later to under two hundred.

Rabies appeared in Israel towards the end of 1976 when twenty six people and an unknown number of animals were bitten by a small white dog that went on a forty hour rampage through the streets of Jerusalem. Tracked down, after the alert had gone out when several people demanded inoculations after being bitten, it was finally shot in the body — because its brain had to be intact to determine whether or not it was rabid. Laboratory tests soon confirmed that it was.

According to Jerusalem's chief veterinary officer, rabies had been advancing slowly from the Golan Heights down the Jordan valley through infected foxes, before it reached the Holy City. The Government declared the whole of Israel and the occupied areas in the Golan, the West Bank and the Gaza Strip "rabies danger arear". The authorities instituted a nation-wide campaign to destroy thousands of stray dogs, cats and foxes. Municipalities in Israel stocked up with hundreds of tins of poisoned meat to deal with stray dogs and cats and clinics built up supplies of anti-rabies vaccine.

Government advertisements warned the public that rabies was a disease not fully conquered by medicine and that it would be fatal if people bitten did not get vaccinated.

## W. H. O'S VIEWS ON CONTROLS

The Sixth Report of the World Health Organisation Expert Committee on Rabies published in 1973 came down in favour of prophylactic vaccination of dogs as being one of the most important weapons in rabies control and urged countries where infected areas exist to adopt vaccination programmes for their canine population.

To standardise procedures throughout the world it recommended that all dogs receive their primary vaccination at the age of three-four months and a booster about one year later. Where puppies of less than three months must be vaccinated, inactivated vaccine should be used followed by revaccination with a potent rabies vaccine as soon as possible after they reach the age of three months.

Because of the scarcity of information on the duration of immunity in cats, they should be revaccinated annually.

Mass vaccination of cattle was recommended in areas where rabies creates serious economic problems and in practice is used chiefly in Latin America against the vampire bat.

The Committee did not recommend using living anti-rabies vaccines in any species of animals where the efficacy for the particular species has not previously been determined. Inactivated vaccine may be used with safety in nearly all species.

Where mass immunization of dogs and cats becomes necessary and this is usually in major metropolitan areas, emphasis should be given to the need for completing the work in the shortest possible time. The use of tags or coloured plastic collars had proved useful in identifying vaccinated animals.

The Report stressed the need for a well conducted proramme for the elimination of strays. This requires the operation of a local pound or similar animal shelter in which animals may be temporarily held and if unclaimed at the end of a short period, destroyed. The practice of making stray and impounded animals available for adoption as pets should be suspended during an outbreak of rabies in a community.

Noting recent increases of reported rabies cases in wild animals acquired as pets and recognizing this possible source of human exposure, the Committee recommended countries either to prohibit the trade in such animals from endemic areas or to introduce adequate quarantine controls combined with vaccination. Similar precautions should be taken when wild animals from infected areas are bought for zoos, exhibitions, medical research or commercial breeding.

The control of rabies can be greatly assisted by the collection and dissemination of information on a world wide basis. As well as the yearly survey of rabies, episodes of more urgent interest such as the appearance of the disease in rabies-free countries are featured in The Weekly Epidemiological Record.

The Expert Committee has produced a case-record from which information is gained for the recording institute and national and international authorities concerned with rabies. Since many problems regarding the prevention and treatment of paralytic accidents, serum sickness and the success or otherwise of post exposure treatment, remain to be solved, the periodic compiling and analysis by World Health Organisation of results obtained in different countries is of great value in assessing the effectiveness of the measures used. The case-record form includes particulars of the person bitten and the animal responsible, the treatment used and the state of the person after six months exposure.

Although most rabies control programmes are conducted on a national basis the work of World Health Organisation has drawn expertise and experience together from all affected areas and could usefully be drawn on when an emergency occurs in an area that has previously been free from the disease.

## Chapter Eleven

# RABIES AND ACTION PLANS FOR THE U.K.

The law — local action plans.

## THE LAW

With the possibility of rabies being introduced into the U.K. becoming more likely as the result of the endemic in Western Europe and more particularly because of its spread across France towards her northern coast, the Government in 1974 introduced the Rabies (Control) Order which laid down a comprehensive procedure for dealing with possible rabies outbreaks. The nature and location of the outbreak would determine which of the powers would be used. One the one hand a case could concern just one infected domestic pet that had had contact with other animals, while on the other the disease might, if a rabid animal had been at large for a period, have infected other pets as well as wild life animals and farm stock. In the first case control would be relatively easy, whereas in the second could prove extremely complex.

The first step that would be taken when there were reasonable grounds for suspecting than an animal was affected with rabies — and it is the duty of anyone discovering such a case to report it to the authorities — would be for the premises where it was kept to be declared an infected place. The animal itself would be secured immediately in as small a confined space as possible, pending examination by a Ministry veterinary officer who, in a high risk case might move it to detention for observation in secure accommodation maintained by the Ministry for such a

*105*

purpose. If the animal has rabies it will die within a few days. The brain would be sent to the Ministry's Central Veterinary Laboratory so that the disease could be confirmed or otherwise.

The follow up action should the diagnosis prove positive will depend on the circumstances. If the animal had been at large with the possibility it had affected other animals The next step would be to declare an infected area round the source of infection — the size of the area would, again, depend on the circumstances. Any or all of the following measures would be introduced.

(a) Restriction of movements of animals into and out of the area.

(b) Control and confinement of animals in the area.

(c) Seizure, detention and disposal of animals not under control in the area.

(d) Compulsory vaccination of animals.

(e) Prohibition of gatherings of animals and sporting and recreational activities, including hunting, racing or coursing of hounds or dogs, point-to-point meetings and the shooting of game or other wild life.

(f) The destruction of foxes, the main wild life vector of the disease in Europe.

Where rabies breaks out amongst wild life in the U.K., control measures would be concentrated on the destruction of foxes in the infected areas. Methods used would be those calculated to be the most effective in the local circumstances and giving the minimum risk to other wild life species and to domestic farm animals.

What in practice would the measures that might be taken in the event of a rabies outbreak, mean? At an infected place a Ministry veterinary inspector could remove any animal affected with or suspected of having rabies, to a place where it can conveniently be kept under observation. He might also take samples to help with the diagnosis and the occupier of the premises would have to give reasonable assistance, and any information in his possession as to the location and movements of any other animal under his charge. Power is given to a veterinary inspector to slaughter any animal in an infected place which has or is suspected of having the disease or has been in contact with such an animal subject to him giving notice to the owner or person in charge.

The Ministry may, where it believes or suspects that rabies exists or has existed within the preceding six months, declare the area to be an infected area. In such an area steps may be taken to destroy foxes other than those held in captivity and authorised persons would be able to enter land for this purpose. Due notice of fox destruction would be given to the occupier of the land and fences or other obstacles might be erected to restrict the movement of animals in and out of the area. Fox carcases would become the property of the Ministry and would be buried or otherwise disposed of as thought fit.

Warning notices might be posted within and on the boundaries of an infected area indicating that the place is an infected area for the purposes connected with the control and eradication of rabies.

Where a large area is involved, there is provision for sub-dividing it into zones and for varying restrictions to be imposed according to the dangers involved. Dogs and cats would have to be securely confined on premises and not allowed to stray but could be exercised away from the home, providing they were leashed and, in the case of dogs, fitted with secure muzzles. They could be moved to other places within the zone if under similar control but would not be allowed to have contact with any other animals at the places to which they are moved.

Animals other than dogs and cats would have to be similarly controlled and under no circumstances allowed to run free. There is no provision for leashing when being exercised, but close control and proper restraint would have to be used.

There would be power to seize and detain any animal not confined or controlled. The local authority would publicly advertise the address of any place where seized animals were detained. A period of three days would be allowed for the owner to claim an animal. He would have to pay the authority's expenses for the work involved and for any additional period of detention a local authority inspector might insist on.

Where an owner failed to meet the expenses or where an animal was unclaimed, the local authority would have power to destroy it. In circumstances where it was found impossible to seize a stray animal, it could be destroyed without capture.

Where vaccination of animals was specified in an infected area, an owner would be given a prescribed period to have his pet injected with a vaccine approved by the Ministry. For identification purposes it would have to be marked in a way the Ministry would require. Failure to carry out vaccination could lead to seizure of the animal which would then be vaccinated or destroyed. Expenses involved in the work would once again be recoverable from the owner.

In an infected area a duty would be imposed on any person who knows of the death of an animal of a species included in the infected area order, to report the fact to a Ministry officer unless he is reasonably sure that it did not die from rabies or that its death had already been reported.

## LOCAL ACTION PLANS

Should an outbreak of rabies occur and involve, for example, domestic animals, humans and wild life, a wide ranging number of officials and professions would be involved. The Ministry has held joint consultations with other government departments, local authorities, police and

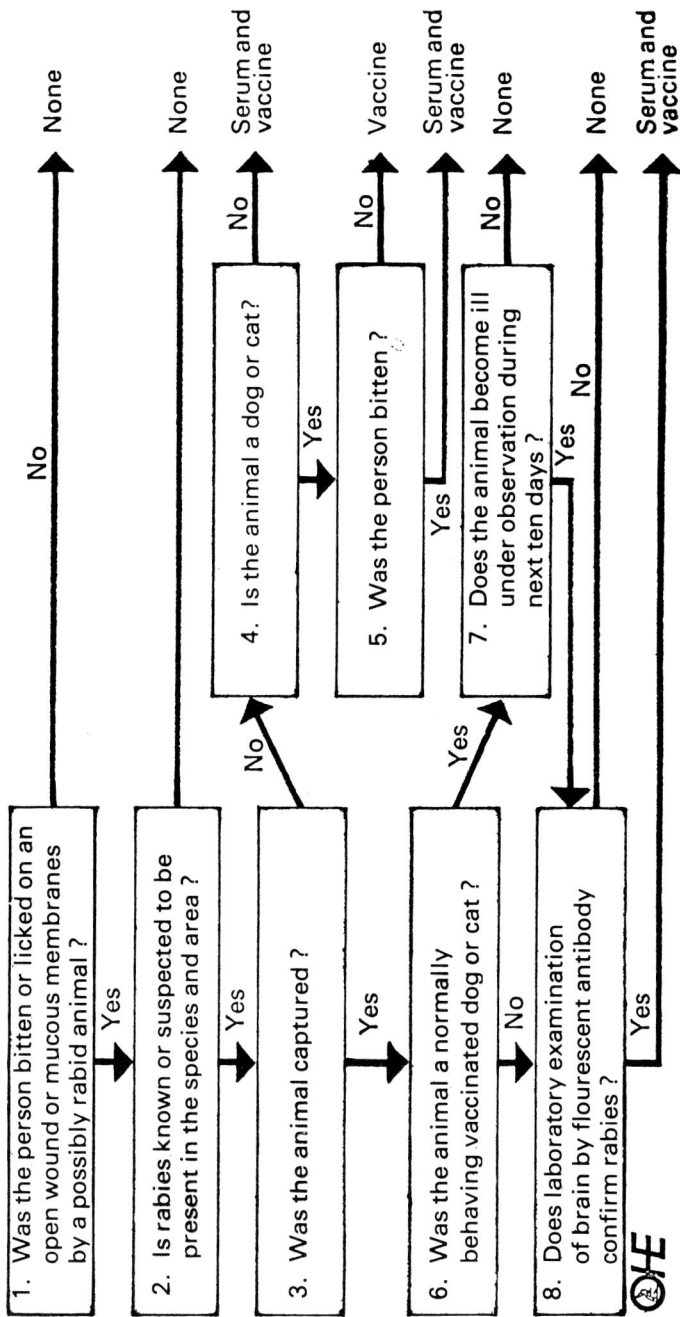

Figure 11—*Decision making in post-exposure rabies treatment*
*Source* Corey and Hattwick 1975

# THE RABIES (Control) ORDER 1974

## Place Rules

**R**ABID ANIMALS KNOWN OR SUSPECTED TO BE REPORTED.

**A**NIMALS TO BE ISOLATED, THEIR DUNG AND BEDDING not TO BE REMOVED.

**B**ANNED TO ALL PERSONS.

**I**NFECTED PLACE TO BE DISINFECTED.

**E**XIT OF ANIMALS DEAD OR ALIVE IS PROHIBITED

**S**IGNS TO BE DISPLAYED.

## Area Provision

1 to 12 Miles

INFECTED PLACE (to be defined)

**I**F NOT UNDER CONTROL ANIMALS TO BE SEIZED.

**N**O MARKETS OR SALES OF ANIMALS.

**F**OXES MAY BE DESTROYED AND OTHER DEFINED ANIMALS.

**E**VERY ANIMAL DEATH TO BE NOTIFIED.

**C**ATS EXERCISED ONLY ON A LEAD.

**T**RUCKED ANIMALS MAY PASS THROUGH.

**E**VERY AND ANY ANIMAL MAY BE VACCINATED.

**D**OGS TO BE ON LEADS AND MUZZLED.

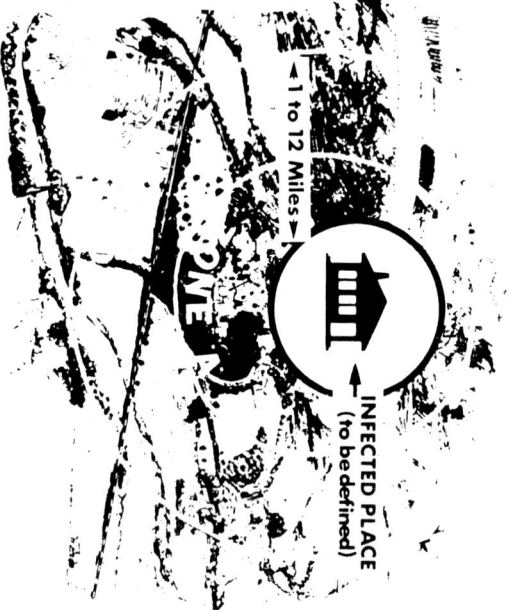

**A**LL ANIMAL MOVEMENT ON LICENCE except CLOSE-RESTRAINED EXERCISE.

**R**ACING, HUNTING AND SHOOTS BANNED.

**E**VERY OR SOME CONDITIONS IN EACH ZONE.

**A**REA TO BE SIGNED.

Figure 12—Rabies (Control) Order 1974. Place Rules and Area Provision. (Poster).

veterinary surgeons, and has issued guidelines on which individual local authorities and the police can base their own local plans.

County Councils through their appropriate departments have been preparing rabies control plans with the object of defining areas of responsibility of the organisations involved and action to be taken by their own officers in the event of a rabies outbreak.

County Councils as diseases of animals authorities are charged with seizing all animals in an infected area that are not under control, placing them in suitable pounds and advertising their locations so that owners may collect them within three days. This duty imposes pracitcal problems involving manpower, vehicles, location, size and construction of pounds, identification of animals detained, feeding and destruction and disposal of animals not claimed. The police would give all the assistance possible but in the event of a major incident it might be necessary to ask for military help.

Publicity during a rabies incident would need to be well informed. Initially it might be prudent to restrict this until the findings of the veterinary inspectors are known. The many organisations involved in an outbreak would each have its own means of publicity. To avoid confusing the public East Sussex County Council would channel all publicity through their own information officer. Good communications to ensure rapid action would be essential and in the case of an infected area would involve the Ministry of Agriculture setting up an incident centre near or within the area to control operations. It is likely that the county council would set up its own mobile facilities close by and the police would probably act in a similar way.

A good varied stock of equipment must be available for use in an emergency. Staff engaged would require protective clothing such as overalls, strong gloves, visors, goggles and wellington boots. To deal with stray animals,

cat nets and dog catchers and portable crates would have to be on hand. Materials needed for use in pounds would include feeding and drinking bowls, disinfectant, tin openers, dog and cat leads, muzzles and fencing materials for pound perimeters.

Although it is possible to make local preparation for a potential rabies incident, the needs at the time involving manpower, premises and equipment will depend to a great extent on the situation that develops and in particular the size of the infected area and whether this is in an open rural area or a densely populated urban one.

## WEST MIDLANDS MOUNT FIRST ANTI—RABIES EXERCISE

Mid-February, 1978 saw the first anti-rabies exercise mounted in Great Britain. Organised by the West Midlands County Council, it lasted for 48 hours when a large part of the town of Halesowen was declared an "infected area".

The exercise involved 100 council staff, officials of the Ministry of Agriculture, Fisheries and Food and the local R.S.P.C.A. inspectorate. The third floor of a multi-storey car park was taken over for use as an animal pound to which were taken 25 stray dogs captured by the band of dog catchers and two cats that had been caught in special traps set in the grounds of a local hospital.

The main purpose of the exercise, which cost some £4,000, was to see how the co-ordination of the various services worked in the field and early reports claimed it to be a big success. There were obviously minor problems to resolve as there would be from any "first time" effort and it is thought this will be the fore runner to other schemes organised on a county basis from which valuable experience will be gained.

## Chapter Twelve

## RABIES AND THOSE INVOLVED

The corporate plan — role of the Ministry vet, small animal vet, the local authority inspector — roles of others involved.

### THE CORPORATE PLAN

Although enforcement of the Rabies (Control) Order 1974 rests largely with the local authority, an uncontained rabies outbreak would require action both to contain its spread and subsequent eradication, and would concern and involve many organisations and their staffs. County councils when considering their local action plans have consulted with their divisional veterinary officer, the police, area health authorities, district councils, private veterinary surgeons and their neighbouring authorities. Working parties were set up and these meet regularly to exchange ideas and clarify each others roles.

### THE ROLE OF THE MINISTRY VET

In normal times the divisional veterinary officer is responsible for distributing his Ministry's posters and leaflets to ensure, as far as possible, that those most exposed to the dangers from a rabid animal and the public in general are aware of the consequences of smuggling in a pet from abroad and the drastic measures that would have to be taken should it develop rabies.

Since the national publicity campaign of 1976, the staffs of divisional veterinary officers have been busy dealing with reports from the public of wild animals, chiefly foxes, seen in suspicious circumstances and abnormal conditions. These have always been concluded as false alarms — it must be remembered that it is most unlikely that rabies would be brought to the U.K. by a rabid wild animal.

The Ministry vet has also been called occasionally to examine a domestic pet where rabies is suspected but usually prefers the animal to be first seen by its owner's veterinary surgeon who will decide if this is necessary.

Should a rabies incident occur in his area, the Ministry vet will be one of the first to be informed and will decide, if the disease is confirmed by his laboratory, what steps should next be taken. He would control the destruction of foxes and any other wild life ordered and the destruction of animals where it is not found possible to seize them. He would be responsible for granting licences for the movement of animals between the zones of an infected area and for permitting the gatherings of animals or certain activities such as hunting, coursing and dog racing. His staff would, if necessary make enquiries of contacts made between the rabid animal and other animals.

## THE ROLE OF THE SMALL ANIMAL VET

The British Small Animal Veterinary Association showed its concern at the constant threat of the reintroduction of rabies by setting up a working party and in 1976 producing a report outlining its role should the event occur.

The responsibilities of the veterinary surgeon employed in small animal practice would be considerable. He would often be the first link in the chain of disease control and not only be called on for a diagnosis but also to act as a general adviser in the fields of prevention and control.

It is obvious that the veterinary surgeon employed in small animal practice will play a unique and vital role in the control of any outbreak of endemic rabies. An early diagnosis will be of prime importance and the responsibility for this aspect will rest almost entirely on his shoulders. His awareness of the symptoms, ability to diagnose and knowledge of the correct investigative procedure will

In this respect he will be the society's watch-dog. He is

obliged by the law to report to a Ministry veterinary officer, local authority diseases of animals inspector or police constable any case of rabies in one of his patients.

He must know how to manage a suspected rabies case and to help and advise his client of his legal obligations. The report suggests that small animal vets should supervise the rigid isolation of the animal until the ''infected place'' notice is served or other decision made. This would mean that adequate isolation facilities must be found in the owner's home or, where the animal has been brought to the vet's premises, in his clinic. Other animals attending the clinic would be treated as possible contacts and although they would be allowed to return home, records of their attendances would be kept.

The Report mentions the possibility that some animal owners might object violently to their pet being impounded on the vet's premises. It is equally possible that there would be owners who would simply release their pet out of fear or ignorance, following the veterinary surgeon's visit to their homes. Achieving effective isolation pending a visit from a Ministry or local authority inspector to decide the next step, is a potential grey area in which the onus is very much on the vet in attendance. It may be that this position should be strengthened by further legislation.

The veterinary practitioner's responsibilities will include the adequate preparation of his staff to meet the threat of rabies. He will instruct them as to the nature of the disease, the handling of animals, the reporting of unusual signs and the approach to suspect animals. He will advise his staff on prophylactic vaccination and first aid treatment after consultation with the district community physician.

## THE ROLE OF THE LOCAL AUTHORITY INSPECTOR

The local authority inspector, known as the diseases of animals inspector, is employed by County Councils usually in either the consumer protection or estates' surveyor's department. His routine duties include the dissemination of publicity literature and he will probably be one of a team that operates a full twenty four hour emergency cover over the country. His main concern with rabies prevention in normal times is in dealing with illegal importations of animals through sea and airports and at small boat marinas. When an animal arrives in this country without its owner previously having obtained a licence, arranged quarantine and authorised carriage, he will interview the person concerned, take statements from witnesses and attend magistrate's or crown court where it is decided to prosecute. He would also arrange for an authorised carrier to take the animal into quarantine or if it its owner decided on destruction make the necessary arrangements with a local veterinary surgeon and afterwards see that the carcase is disposed of by incineration. The owner would also be given the alternative of re-exporting the animal and the inspector would issue an export notice, requiring this to be done.

He may receive a report that a foreign yacht has tied up in a harbour or marina with a dog or cat on board. Although a Customs Officer will board the boat and explain our rabies regulations, the local authority inspector will pay visits to see that the animal is not allowed on deck or be exercised ashore.

A diseases of animals inspector may also be called on to help with a pet that has developed unusual symptoms akin to rabies or follow up reports of animals seen in cars with foreign registration numbers.

In an emergency the local authority inspector is one of three people who may receive notification of a rabid or suspect rabid animal. He will visit the premises and first see that the animal or carcase is isolated from any other animal, making sure that no one touches it. He will then inform the divisional veterinary officer, the officer in charge of the local police station and the head of his department.

It is then his job to issue an Infected Place notice on the

occupier of the premises; also on the occupier of any premises where there is an animal that might have been exposed to infection. These will remain in force until varied or cancelled by a further written notice served by a Ministry veterinary inspector.

He will assist the divisional veterinary officer in tracing animal and human contacts made by the suspected rabid animal and, in an infected area, will serve confinement notices on owners of animals affected by the order.

## ROLES OF OTHERS INVOLVED

Area Health authorities, through their district community physicians, would receive reports of all biting and scratching incidents involving humans and arrange for vaccinations where necessary.

Two Sussex environmental health departments are keeping records of all fox earths in their districts. These are being pin-pointed on maps by means of flags and their known locations would obviously be of value in any programme of fox destruction that might become necessary. Rabies has been made a notifiable disease and any cases in man would involve environmental health officers in conjunction with area health authorities but their exact role has not yet been determined by the Department of Health and Social Services.

If a suggestion of the Department of Environment Working Party on Dogs that a responsibility for stray dogs should be transferred from the Police to district councils is adopted and dog wardens appointed, the latter would be responsible for impounding strays.

This would greatly lessen the work of County Councils who would have to deal with the problem in an outbreak of rabies.

The police would obviously play an important role, being equipped for, and experienced in dealing with similar problems and the enforcement of the law.

## Chapter Thirteen

## RABIES AND CURRENT TRENDS AND THOUGHTS

Oil rigs — education — treatment in man — the Law and smugglers — control of dogs — pets on foreign boats — new anti-rabies suits — compensation for slaughter — pets in jail.

### OIL RIGS

The Ministry of Agriculture has gone so far as to consider the possibility of an animal being imported from an oil rig— a comparatively new feature of our seascape. Any animal landed from one of these structures would be subject to the normal six months quarantine requirement whether or not it had come from outside territorial waters or had had contact with "foreign" animals. H.M. Customs and port authorities have been made aware of the situation and appropriate enforcement measures are taken at ports used by vessels which service oil rigs. Although there could be a temptation for an oil rig worker to keep a pet for company, the Ministry considers there is no evidence to suggest that oil rigs present a loophole in our anti-rabies defences.

### EDUCATION

As a result of the national publicity campaign of 1976 the subject received wide coverage by means of leaflets, posters, newspaper and magazine articles, lectures and talks and features on radio and television and must have reached the greater proportion of the population. Although the propaganda appeared to have successfully put over the danger of rabies to the public there were those who considered it too sensational and not properly balanced.

The British Small Animal Veterinary Association's Report, while acknowledging the necessity of an education programme, stressed the need for presenting the material rationally and without spectacular sensation treatment

116

that simply contributes to rabiphobia. The urgency of the situation has to be stressed but it should be balanced against the practical measures of rabies control.

The Report said that schools must be involved in educational programmes, for children present a special risk. At the moment prevention is the only logical method of defence and children must be made aware that the most serious risk is the illegally imported animal. Those who have been involved in dealing with the landing of small pets such as mice, guinea pigs and gerbills, will know the heartaches that can arise from ignorance of the law. It is important that children know why we operate current import and quarantine measures; also for them to learn an understanding of the nature of rabies and what life would be like in this country if the disease reappeared. It is equally important to educate children not to fondle dogs, cats and other small animals while on holiday abroad. It is a natural instinct to do so and only continuous education can ensure they are kept aware of the possible dangers if they succumb to the temptation.

## TREATMENT OF RABIES IN MAN

Although the World Health Organisation Expert committee on Rabies hold out no expectation of a miracle for the disease, it feels that modern means of treatment might provide some hopes for recovery. A rabid patient, it says, should be isolated in an intensive medical care unit and treated along the following lines :—

Anxiety and pain can be relieved by liberally using sedatives in a quiet environment.

Respiratory function can be continued by tracheotomy and artificial respiration.

Drugs with a curare-like action can be employed to deal with spastic muscular contractions.

Hydration and diuresis can be dealt with by intravenous perfusions and diuretics.

Constant monitoring is necessary to prevent heart failure.

## THE LAW AND SMUGGLERS

Despite the increases in penalties brought in under the 1974 Rabies Importation Order, which included a maximum fine of four hundred pounds in a magistrate's court and up to a year's imprisonment and/or an unlimited fine in a crown court for a deliberate attempt to evade the regulations, the Government's publicity campaign so awakened public feeling, that there were numerous calls for the penalties to be even stiffer. Among suggestions made were the automatic imprisonment for long periods for offenders and the raising of the maximum four hundred pounds fine that can be imposed by magistrates, to one thousand pounds. The Government has promised legislation to cover the latter. Towards the end of his period of office the then Prime Minister Harold Wilson agreed that fines of four hundred pounds were totally inadequate because of the risks to life and the risks of terrible suffering in this country.

The Government has also been urged to revise diplomatic immunity laws in the case of rabies. At present more than four thousand foreigners living in embassies in London cannot be prosecuted for breaches of the rabies regulations. In one case that came to light, the embassy concerned sent the diplomat home and the pet was placed in quarantine. Members of parliament feared that embassies would not always be so cooperative and felt it was wrong to be totally dependent on their attitude. The opposition spokesman for Health wanted diplomats who smuggle in animals to face prosecution like anyone else.

Although local authority inspectors are empowered to destroy animals illegally imported, the provision is optional and not mandatory. They have to keep uppermost in mind the extent of the risk that such an animal is creating. There would be grounds for destruction if there was no secure place to hold the animal and there was an escape risk or in a situation of potential contact with humans or animals. Destruction might also be considered if there was no way of ensuring that the authority would be reimbursed with any costs of carriage, vaccination and quarantine of an animal. However in a situation where an illegally imported animal could safely be dealt with by re-exportation, or by being directed to authorised quarantine premises and the owner is able to meet the costs, it might be difficult to justify destruction on rabies security grounds.

The national publicity campaign prompted suggestions of a stronger line in a number of letters to the press. Many people felt that if an animal smuggler knew his pet would automatically be put down this would act as a far greater deterrent than a possible fine. Such a suggestion was made in the House of Lords but the Deputy Chief Whip said the Government considered that the discretionary powers of local authorities were sufficient.

An even direr measure was suggested by The Looker-On in Blackwood's Magazine who said that rather than fine or imprison dog smugglers, they should be made to suffer the series of fourteen inoculations in the stomach — he feared, however, that some court or commission on human rights would object!

Among the views of the Association of District Councils sent to the relevant Government departments were suggestions that the illegal importation of animals should be made an arrestable offence and that H.M. Customs should be urged to use the powers already available to them to confiscate private vehicles in which animals were concealed for illegal importation into this country.

## CONTROL OF DOGS

The highlighting of the threat of rabies, a disease long associated in the public mind with the dog and hydrophobia, inevitably brought to the surface other problems attributable to man's best friend. Public opinion hardened against the nuisance caused by the fouling of streets and open spaces. The disease toxicariasis, which can be transmitted to humans from the faeces of unwormed dogs, received considerable publicity in 1976. It was said at the time that about eight per cent of both domestic and stray dogs carried the infection which has been known in rare cases to cause blindness in a child. It was estimated, on a dog population of six point six million that about a quarter of a million tons of solid waste was being deposited each year, much of which was to be found in parks, recreation grounds and other public places where children play.

One suggestion to lessen the problem was to lower the dog population by disposing of strays and other unwanted animals. An Inter-Departmental Working Party which produced its report in August 1976 recommended the appointment by district councils of dog wardens (one to fifty thousand population) who would be empowered to check licences, investigate nuisances and offences and impound or dispose of strays. The cost of the service would be met by increasing the licence fee to Five pounds. Other recommendations dealt with control of breeding and road safety. There seems little chance however that the recommendations will be acted on in the present financial climate.

There is no doubt that the great increase in the dog population in recent years has created a real need for stricter control and elimination of the stray who not only fouls public places and causes thousands of road accidents each year, but who would present one of the biggest hazards to the spread of rabies should it reach this country.

One authority which has taken positive steps to control stray dogs, is the borough of Afan which is centred around the South Wales town of Port Talbot. In an article in District Council Review, the council's public relations officer, Terry Thomas, describes action during the first three months of the campaign which followed the introduction of the Control of Dogs Order in October 1976.

The council had, since June 1974, followed a policy of impounding stray animals such as sheep, 'cattle and horses and decided to extend the scheme to stray dogs. 85 dogs were impounded during the first three months by the borough's "dog catchers", of which 36 were reclaimed by their owners. The majority were collected within 48 hours suggesting to the author a genuine concern for the welfare of the wayward pet.

The problem of straying animals in Afan is so great that the council's two dog catchers double up as shepherds in the animal impounding unit of the borough surveyor's department. In the rural parts of the borough, the incidence of lost and straying animals is so high that it led to the appointment of the two shepherds and a working party comprising councillors, farmers, landowners and other local people who are all helping to keep the problem within reasonable bounds.

It is in the town of Port Talbot that a real problem exists with stray dogs. Complaints had poured in to the council offices of dogs running loose, damaging property, fouling pavements and roaming the streets in snarling packs.

The Council decided to take positive steps to combat the nuisance and to implement the Control of Dogs on Roads Order, aimed at ensuring that all dogs are kept on leads on roads in the borough and rendering the owners of dogs impounded under the order liable to prosecution. Afan was one of the very few local authorities to tackle the stray dog menace with its own animal impounding unit. The bright yellow landrover and trailer specially equipped for dog catching is now a familiar sight to Afan residents as it patrols the borough's 40,000 acres on the lookout for stray dogs which are rounded up and impounded at the council's kennels.

Owners can collect their pets on payment of a £2

impounding fee plus the expense of the dog's keep while in the council's care — currently 65p a day. In addition, a charge is made for V.A.T. and administration. Strays collected by the unit are kept for up to a week and, if not claimed, handed over to R.S.P.C.A. for disposal.

Mr Thomas commented that the number of strays in the U.K. continues to rise sharply to an estimated current figure of 1 million with many more unwelcome or uncared for by their owners. Widespread publicity given to the Order plus the presence of the unit's vehicle on the streets of Afan, has brought about a greater awareness of the problem. Both the council and the R.S.P.C.A. who approve the new scheme, would prefer to rely on the co-operation and commonsense of dog owners to keep their pets under control rather than have them caught and impounded in the authority's kennels. One irresponsible dog owner can cause more damage than a dozen well trained and cared for animals. For the minority who allow their dogs to roam the roads of Afan uncontrolled, the warning is "Look Out, Look out, There's a Dog Catcher About".

## PETS ON FOREIGN BOATS

One of the biggest sources of danger that the country faces in keeping rabies out is from the pets being brought ashore from small boats moored in yacht harbours. In an attempt to plug the gap, the National Yacht Harbour Association sent out letters to boating organisations throughout Europe asking their members to observe our rabies control regulations. The extent of the possible problem becomes apparent when it was learnt that some four hundred visitors a day arrive by small boat in the height of the holiday season.

The letter pointed out that private yachts from abroad with animals on board should be directed to the nearest port with health check facilities and the police should be informed. It would then be for the Port Health Authority to say whether the animal could be quarantined, with safety on board. The craft should fly a quarantine flag and the police kept informed of any intended movements. The vessel should not be allowed to go aground or berth alongside the shore or another vessel. Any breach should be an arrestable offence and the vessel could be forfeited and the animal destroyed. The scheme received Government approval pending legislation.

East Sussex County Council have provided a portable kennel at Rye harbour. Any animal aboard a boat which puts into harbour is placed in the kennel and only freed when the boat sails again.

Littlehampton Harbour Board, among others, has provided a special mooring for boats needing constant surveillance and the district council has declared the harbour area a pest and animal control zone under the supervision of a pest control officer.

The Channel Island of Alderney, not regarded by our rabies regulations as "foreign", took the drastic step of banning the entry of all animals from Great Britain which can carry rabies, unless they had a special licence. This extension of the Island's rabies control order, which also included animals brought from Ireland, the Isle of Man and other Channel Isles, was found necessary because Alderney's harbourmaster was having great difficulty in confirming the last ports of call of visiting boats. Alderney being only eight miles from the French coast and a popular centre for Cherbourg yachtsmen, it was feared that free entry could be a loophole through which animals could enter the British anti-rabies area.

## NEW ANTI RABIES SUITS

Harbour transport police, who might be the first men in action, should a rabid animal get away in a harbour or marina area, have been issued with special anti rabies gear. The equipment made from soft leather, consists of leggings, a coat, heavy industrial gauntlets and head-gear. The face will be protected by a visor with a Perspex screen.

The set, which costs about sixty pounds, has been issued to policemen in all British Rail and Sea Link ports in the U.K. to keep out rabid animal saliva from which they could contract the disease if it penetrated into a cut or open wound.

## COMPENSATION FOR RABIES SLAUGHTER

As a further step in the development of contingency plans to deal with any possible outbreaks of rabies, an Order was laid before Parliament early in 1977 prescribing the rates of compensation to be paid for animals which have to be compulsorily slaughtered. For the purpose a rabies outbreak would be one that occurred outside quarantine premises.

Where an animal was affected with rabies at the time of its slaughter compensation would be payable at the rate of fifty per cent of its market value immediately before it contracted the disease. In all other cases the compensation would be the full market value of the animal immediately before slaughter. Nothing would be paid in respect of an animal imported illegally.

## PETS IN JAIL

More than two hundred inmates of San Quentin Prison were ordered out on New Year's Day 1977 — all prisoner's pets. Cats, lizards, mice, rats, snakes, gold-fish and birds were being kept but some two thousand odd prisoners who had none, began complaining about those who did — especially when a fellow cell-mate's cat was found sleeping on their pillow. Not only was sanitation a problem but whenever a prisoner was bitten by a cat he was forced to have a series of rabies injections. Fights broke out among the inmates and on the appointed day eighty cats were handed over to visitors while the remaining miscellany of pets were either set free or destroyed.

## *A NEW, SAFE TRANSIT PEN*

The threat of rabies to our shore has brought about a number of developments in the field of equipment designed to deal with rabid or rabid suspect animals and strays. Among the more sophisticated is a light weight aluminium transit pen manufactured by Cartonlite Limited of Mansfield, Notts which can be used in conjuction with a noose pole or purse net.

The pen, weighing 70 lbs, has a double compartment with an attachable dividing panel and sliding trap and detachable canopy net for segration or collective retention of cats and smaller animals. Alternatively one compartment only can be used.

The pen has been designed with the safety of the operator foremost in mind and animals remain under control completely until secured inside the pen which is fitted with sliding handles for ease of end or side lifting.

Ventilation at the top is of double safety mesh against claw scratching and the pen can be quickly dismantled for transport in a car boot or for storage purposes.

The noosepole for dog catching has a sliding friction grip with a remote noose releasing mechanism so that the animal can be released from the noose within the pen and under control. The nylon purse net revolves to lock in the open or closed position.

## *HUMANE DESTRUCTION*

In the event of a rabies incident involving the rounding up of stray animals, a quick and humane method of destruction is necessary in the case of those which are not claimed by their owners.

M. D. Components of Luton, Beds have devised a chloroform chamber for the humane destruction of cats and other small animals and an electrocution chamber for dogs. The former is constructed of chipboard covered with Sefenite plastic, impervious to water and urine, and scratch resistant. The observation window is of clear glass and the hinges, catches and vents are constructed from a non–ferrous type metal which cannot rust or corrode.

The Huelec cabinet for the humane electrocution of dogs is recommended by the R.S.P.C.A., the Battersea Dogs Home and the Ulster S.P.C.A. and measures highest in the equipment field of this kind when considering the six requirements laid down by the British Veterinary Association. These are painlessness, reliability, rapidity, safeness and simplicity of operation and the desirability of the method appearing humane as well as actually being so.

The control unit section, which is removable while the dog is in transit, is constructed of 18 s.w.g. mild steel sheet welded case with plastic control panel fully instrumented. The cabinet is of similar construction to the cat chamber while the observation window is of armoured glass and the cabinet is illuminated when the doors are closed. The latter are provided with safety interlock switches which disconect the mains supply when the doors are open.

The cabinet is designed first to stun the dog by passing an electric current through its brain and subsequently to kill it while still unconscious by passing a second current through the body to stop the heart.

It is reassuring to know that humane methods of destruction, should the occasion arise, are available to diseases of animals authorities whose painful duty would be to put down unclaimed strays in an infected area.

## SKYTRAIN LOOPHOLE TIGHTENED

The recently introduced "walk on" Skytrain service to New York's Kennedy Airport, from which two passengers have already been caught smuggling pets into Britain, prompted a flying visit to the U.S.A. by two members of

West Sussex County Council's trading standards department.

The new service where 300 or so people queue to get on a flight the same day brought fears of a greater danger to animals being brought into the U.K. illegally. As a result of the visit there has been a general tightening up of procedures on the other side of the Atlantic. Now, rabies warnings are announced to passengers on board aircraft and notices displayed at ticket and check-in desks.

## KEEN DEMAND FOR RABIES - FREE FOX FURS

The Looker-On, writing in Blackwood's Magazine, claims that rabies is indirectly posing a more serious threat to the extinction of foxes in Great Britain and Ireland than other factors. Apparently a fashion for fox furs is sweeping Europe at the same time as the spread of rabies and Continental furriers are prepared to pay £20 a fox if it is guaranteed rabies free.

Foxes, therefore it is claimed, are being shot, trapped and poisoned in large numbers on this side of the Channel by persons using such sophisticated equipment as transistors that reproduce a rabbit's squeal so as to lure foxes within range.

## Chapter Fourteen

## RABIES AND THE FRENCH SCENE 1976

Setting the scene — projects in the study field — patterns of rabies in north-east France — rabies in French livestock.

## SETTING THE SCENE

Because rabies is spreading across France and is likely to reach its northern coast in the forseeable future and because that area is closest to the shores of Great Britain, our Government is keeping an anxious eye on what is happening on the other side of the Channel.

France has lived with the disease for nearly a decade and the profound effect it has had on town and country life there, serves well to illustrate the problems that might arise should it find its way here. Everyone is at risk — not only the native inhabitant — be he farmer, pet owner, huntsman or child — but the itinerant holiday maker as well. A rabies endemic affects them all in one way or another.

To date more than twenty five per cent of French departments—the equivalent of English counties—have intected area in their midst and the authorities believe that eventually rabies will spread throughout the country. At the present time it is confined in the north east but since it crossed the Belgian and West German borders in 1968, has spread in a 250 miles arc and is found in new departments every year.

Rabies costs the French government millions of francs a year. As each area becomes infected, special rabies units are set up by the state veterinary service. The hub of operations is at Nancy where the national study centre was

*128*

opened in 1968. Here is situated the main rabies diagnosis centre and the office that deals with the dissemination of information on the disease. All new vaccines are tested and a long term research programme is being conducted into how the virus is kept alive in the habitats of wild animals.

## PROJECTS IN THE STUDY FIELD

Michael Gaisford, a staff writer with *Farmers Weekly,* has visited infected areas in France and spoken to leading veterinarians about there work. Dr Louis Andral, a world expert on rabies and head of the Centre D'Etudes sur La Rage who worked on control of the disease in F*hiopia and Morocco before taking over the fight against rabies in France in 1968, thinks it inevitable that foxes will ultimately spread the disease through his country. He sees his prime role as informing farmers and the general public on ways of lessening the risks to themselves and their livestock and pets. He hopes that by encouraging fox control, the spread of the disease may be slowed down. In the long term, he believes it might be possible to eradicate it from wild life when there emerges a clearer understanding of its characteristics.

To this end studies are proceeding at Nancy on how rabies exists in wild life when foxes are absent from an area, the density of foxes and their relationship with other species and the possibility of fox vaccination. One idea being investigated is that ticks or fleas living in fox lairs might harbour the virus. Ferrets are being used to study the ticks usually associated with foxes as well as, in some cases, captive foxes.

Dr Andral believes that one day there will be a human death from rabies, probably resulting from carelessness or ignorance. He sees no reason why it should spread to Britain providing our import controls are strictly adhered to. Domestic animal control, he says, is fairly easy. It would be extremely difficult for rabies to enter Britsh wild-life from infected Continental foxes.

One of the biggest problems is public co-operation. In some areas all possible cases of the disease are reported but, because of what follows when its presence is notified, there is less co-operation in others. Where rabies occurs in farm animals a three month ban on the movement of stock and milk from the farm is imposed. This acts as a deterrent to some farmers when they should report a rabies incident.

Rabies is no advertisement for tourism and an over zealous town mayor might find it affects his support when he next comes up for election.

## PATTERNS OF RABIES IN NORTH EAST FRANCE

The departments of Meurthe and Moselle, which border Belgium and West Germany and where rabies first entered France in 1968, has the longest French experience of the disease. Its pattern in this area was decribed to Mr Gaisford by the departemnt's Chief Veterinary Officer Henri Rocq. During 1969, seventy six cases were reported, in the north of his area. A slow advance of ten miles and seventy cases were reported in 1970 and it was thought that the disease might have been contained. The next year, however, saw an explosion, rabies developing throughout the area with two hundred and seventeen cases. In 1972 there were two hundred cases and these were restricted to the south. The following year, the disease moved back to the north and was responsible for one hundred and eighty four cases. In 1974, (ninety nine cases) and 1975 (eighty three cases) the south was chiefly affected, and most incidents involved foxes.

In 1976, after an interval of three years, rabies re-appeared in the north with over three hundred cases, fifty of which were in cows. Mr Rocq thinks that the large number of cows affected was due to farmers thinking that the disease had left the area and ceasing to vaccinate their stock against the virus.

While the disease was in the area most farmers vaccinated their animals. Because of the cost and because
vaccination was not made compulsory, many ceased the
practice when outbreaks in foxes died down. In France,
rabies vaccine is usually given at the same time as the
compulsory anti foot and mouth injection and costs the
equivalent of one pound twenty five pence per animal.

Mr Rocq does not believe in total fox destruction. He
would like to see the fox population brought down to less
than one to five hundred acres and, at the same time, to
encourage a high level of vaccination of farm stock. To
help him with the fox problem the Federation des Chasseurs
employ sixteen gamekeepers throughout his department.
To augment shooting, gassing, particularly of young foxes in
their dens, is carried out in the spring, using chloropicrine
gas.

Mr Rocq's biggest job is to follow up daily reports of
cases of rabies. A flying squad of vans, based at Malzeville
near Nancy, is on permanent watch waiting for calls to
collect dead foxes, other species and domestic pets
where death from rabies is suspected. The team may deal
with half a dozen cases a day in the height of summer.
Where there has been no contact between the dead animal
and a human, diagnosis is carried out at Dr Andral's
laboratory. In cases when a person has been bitten by a
suspect rabid dog the work is carried out at the Pasteur
Institute. The work involves examination of a sample of
brain cells from the suspect animal. Cells are injected
into white mice and the effects observed.

Mr Rocq's department deals mainly with foxes but in
certain instances rabid foxes have been killed by dogs.
Where this happens the dog is destroyed without question
even if it has been vaccinated against rabies. In an infected
area a dog lover, therefore, runs a great risk of losing
his pet if he lets it loose in the country where there is access

to wild-life.

Any cow which dies of suspected rabies after a fox bite is taken straight away to a special knackers yard in Nancy. A brain sample is taken to confirm whether or not the animal is rabid. Where a positive dianosis is confirmed an order restricting movement of stock from the farm for three months is served. A similar ban is imposed on any milk produced on the premises.

The farmer is advised to contact his local doctor who may offer a course of anti rabies vaccinations. However, Mr Rocq said "cows don't bite and it is usually sufficient for the farmer to wash thoroughly and disinfect himself".

In an effort to see that farmers placed in such situations do not sell any of their cows and to be able to trace them if he does, a record of the ear tags of all cows on the farm is sent to veterinary headquarters after an outbreak.

Mr Rocq's team of eight, working on rabies, are vaccinated regularly against the disease. Although fifty out of a quarter of a million cattle in his area were killed by rabies in 1976 he considers it less of a potential hazard than foot and mouth disease, a condition he has not seen during the past fifteen years.

## RABIES IN FRENCH LIVE STOCK

Experience in France indicates that isolated outbreaks of rabies in pets can be dealt with quickly without further spread but once established in wild-life, particularly in foxes, there is a continuing risk to farm live-stock that have not been vaccinated.

The importance of the disease in the different species can well be seen by a table showing the break-down of the one thousand nine hundred and eight cases that occurred in France from January to August of 1976 :—

It will be seen that, next to foxes, the highest incidence of rabies in any animal, including the dog and cat, in France that year, was in cattle.

*Rabies—You and Your Pets*

*Wild Animals*

| | |
|---|---:|
| Foxes | 1,584 |
| Badgers | 22 |
| Deer | 4 |
| Other species | 32 |

*Farm Live-stock*

| | |
|---|---:|
| Cattle | 84 |
| Sheep and goats | 52 |
| Horses | 14 |
| Pigs | 2 |

*Domestic Animals*

| | |
|---|---:|
| Dogs | 45 |
| Cats | 69 |

## Chapter Fifteen

## RABIES AND ANIMALS ON THE FARM

Association with humans — incidence in farm animals — symptoms in farm animals — action after rabies contact.

## *ASSOCIATION WITH HUMANS*

There are a few reported cases of man contacting rabies from the bite or saliva of a farm animal affected with the disease. The dumb form of rabies in cows often leads farmers to imagine that the animal is choking as a result of swallowing a fairly large object. Attempts to locate and extract it have sometimes proved fatal. It is a relatively easy matter for the skin covering the fingers to be pierced by the cow's teeth in its distress, allowing the virus to enter the system via the animal's saliva. In 1959 a Canadian farmer infected himself in this way and subsequently died of rabies. The majority of people treated in Canada for bites from suspect animals in 1970, followed attacks from rabid cattle.

Two decades ago thirty two Argentinians received treatment after being bitten or exposed in other ways to infection from cattle. Nineteen received treatment after bites from swine and thirteen following attacks by rabid horses during the same year.

Mistaking rabies for gall sickness and, in endeavours to hold the tongue for ease of dosing, South African farmers have been known to expose cut hands to infected cattle saliva.

In 1970 no fewer than three thousand and two cases of bites from farm animals were recorded by the World Health Organisation in figures notified to the Ankara Rabies Institute alone. A number of other cases were reported that year in the Istanbul and Izmir areas of Turkey.

*134*

## INCIDENCE IN FARM ANIMALS

Farm animals which are confined and reared under intensive conditions are more prone to attack by a rabid animal than those which are allowed to range freely. Heavy losses have been experienced in American premises where large numbers of beef cattle are fattened under a zero-grazing system.

Almost invariably cattle become infected with rabies following bites on the head or face in many cases by rabid dogs and foxes. It has been noted that cattle are prone to attack from dogs and foxes that infiltrate their feeding grounds and the latter may, in some cases, retaliate in self defence as much as being the aggressor.

The skunk may be the means of passing on the disease among cattle in the U.S.A. while in South Africa an expert is quoted as saying "There is a history of a mad mongoose associated with cattle rabies cases".

The transmissions of the paralytic form of rabies by vampire bats, at one time caused over fifty per cent losses among Mexican cattle. The disease was, at that time, the chief cause of death among ranch cattle in Central and Southern America. Mass vaccination carried out as a result of the problem, has proved successful in achieving a steady decline in the number of cases.

The vampire, a nocturnal mammal lives in farm buildings in the day time, emerging at night to wreak havoc among the cattle, biting the head, neck and back and living off the blood. Attacks have been countered by wiring in buildings and leaving lights burning all night. In Tobago and Trinidad where horses as well as cattle are preyed on by the vampire, the former are vaccinated once a year against the disease.

A major outbreak of rabies in cattle in Yugoslavia was introduced by rabid wolves and caused a major incident in 1956. The Canadian figures for 1967 show a total of five hundred and sixteen farm animals having died from rabies, as follows :—

Cattle 417, Sheep 52, Pigs 32 and Horses 15.

*SYMPTOMS IN FARM ANIMALS*

In horses rabies often produces fits of agression and madness.  The animals may attack stable fittings, other horses and humans.  Occasionally they mutilate themselves. Between fits of aggression, an animal may be restless, move its ears in all directions and exhibit spasmodic contractions of the face muscles.  The tail may be carried high and stiff giving the mistaken impression of tetanus.  Later the animal becomes unsteady on its feet.  Death usually occurs some four days after the onset and after an agitated death struggle.

In cattle the first symptom, which may be missed by the herdsman, may be one of depression.  Loss of appetite and a drop in the milk yield may follow.  Frequent lowing throughout the twenty four hours is on a harsh note.  In the female animal there is an impression of being on heat. There can be signs of colic accompanied by the drawing of wind through the anus, constipation, straining, and the absence of rumination.

When paralysis affects the pharynx, swallowing becomes impossible, and thick saliva often runs from the mouth, fouling the head and neck.  Paralysis then affects the muscles of the lower jaw so that it can be dislocated laterally. The same condition of the neck muscles enables the head to be moved without difficulty.

Paralysis of the fore-quarters is common and usually precedes that of the hind-quarters.  The animal may be found to have fallen on its breast with its neck fully extended on the ground.  This form of the paralytic type of rabies usually lasts from from four to ten days, while in the furious form, there is immediate aggressiveness towards man and, occasionally, dogs.

In some cases that develop from three to four days, there are no typical symptoms to be seen apart from the change in the normal tone of the lowing and some difficulty with movement. It is not surprising that such a form of rabies could be mistaken for other metabolic forms of cattle disease. In Trinidad in 1925 paralysis of the jaw and tongue was associated with botulism, a bacterial disease that produced similar symptons with an inability to swallow.

Because they are relatively inconspicuous, sheep, goats and pigs who have contracted rabies, may go unnoticed. In sheep and goats, the symptons may be like those found in cattle but often little may be noticed apart from some kind of upset of the digestive system followed by paralysis. In a classic case in England in the 1800's an outbreak of the furious type of rabies among sheep was described thus :—
"The rabid ewes trotted back and forth, biting at hurdles, tearing mouthfuls of wool out of each other, foaming at the mouth".

Pigs with rabies rarely attack humans but usually squeal and become excitable and nervous. Their tails may twitch and there may be muscular spasms of the head and jaw, Paralysis and death follow.

## ACTION AFTER RABIES CONTACT

Dr R. K. Sikes in his "Guidelines for the Control of Rabies" recommended that immediate slaughter should be carried out where a farm animal has been bitten by a known rabid animal. The carcase and any milk should be condemned as unfit for human consumption. He suggests it is safe to use an animal for human food if it is slaughtered within a week of being bitten. Slaughtermen exposed to rabid animals should always wear gloves and avoid being contaminated by the bitten area. A large amount of the tissue surrounding the bite should be rejected as unfit. The remainder of the carcase would be considered safe.

Chapter Sixteen

RABIES AND A SWITCH IN QUARANTINE

Unique case — Investigations — The Court Case — Costs.

## UNIQUE CASE

In a case believed to be unique in the annals of diseases of animals legislation a Hove doctor was found guilty at Winchester Assizes on October 1st 1979 of removing his pet cat Biba from quarantine kennels at Farringdon, Hants and substituting it with one he had obtained from the R.S.P.C.A. in Brighton. He was fined £1,000, given a three months suspended prison sentence and ordered to pay £1,000 towards the cost of the case. He also faces possible action by the General Medical Council to whom a report is sent by the police for consideration by its penal committee.

## KITTENS GIVE GAME AWAY

Suspicions were aroused some fifteen months earlier when, to the consternation of the staff, a cat in quarantine at Kitcombe Kennels gave birth to kittens. The records showed the cat to be a spayed female registered as Biba and belonging to Dr Peter Holden, a locum doctor, living in Hove. It had been admitted ninety days before the birth but the gestation period of a cat is 60 to 70 days at the outside, and in addition, all male cats resident in the kennels at the time had been neutered.

## INVESTIGATIONS

After the birth of the kittens the proprietor of the kennels alerted the local authorities involved—Hampshire and East Sussex County Councils. The writer was the duty diseases of animals inspector for the latter authority on the day in question and was instructed to make enquiries at the doctor's home in Hove. These revealed that there were a black and white kitten and a black and white cat owned by the Holdens at Hove, but the latter could not be produced at

138

the time.

On being questioned Dr Holden said the cat had originally been bought in this country and spayed by a Brighton veterinary surgeon. The family had lived in Zambia for a while before moving on to South Africa from whence the cat was sent home in advance of the Holdens and placed in quarantine. The cat he had at Hove was one he had obtained from the R.S.P.C.A. in Brighton.

Later, contact with the R.S.P.C.A. revealed that the cat had been taken by Dr Holden on May 12th 1978, the same day that he made his last visit to the Kitcombe establishment.

As the pieces of the jigsaw began to fit together, it was decided to seize the cat at Hove after which it was taken to quarantine kennels at Albourne in West Sussex.

Tests carried out on both cats revealed that the cat from Hove, alleged to have been obtained from the R.S.P.C.A. had been vaccinated against rabies—animals coming into quarantine receive this treatment as a matter of routine but the procedure is not used on animals who have never left the country.

After statements had been taken from all those involved, it was decided to prosecute Dr Holden and to entrust the work to Hampshire County Council in whose area the alleged offence had occurred.

## THE COURT CASE

Dr Holden appeared before Alton Magistrates Court on December 12th 1978 and was committed to Winchester Assizes for an alleged breach of the Rabies Order 1974.

The case at Winchester Crown Court headlined in the national press as "The Copy Cat" case, opened on September 24th 1979. The prosecution alleged that Dr Holden. who had placed his cat in quarantine the previous April, and whose family were devoted to the animal could bear the separation no longer than a month. He had obtained a similar cat from the Brighton R.S.P.C.A, taken it to Kitcombe and removed his own. The cats were sufficiently alike for the kennel staff to be completely taken in and it was not until the kittens arrived that suspicions were aroused.

Mr John Smyth Q.C. prosecuting, said that it was a most serious breach of the anti-rabies law, Rabies was a killer of animals and sometimes fatal in human beings and the most stringent precautions were taken to prevent the disease from entering Britain.

Dr Holden said that he had obtained the cat from the R.S.P.C.A. to console his wife while Biba was in quarantine.

The two cats had been held at Kitcombe and Albourne respectively pending the case and were produced in court on the second day of the trial in an 'identicat' parade to help the jury decide whether a swap had been carried out.

Further evidence showed that the day after the alleged substitution, vets. discovered that the cat at Kitcombe had gingivitis, a life-long intermittent inflammation of the gums and eyelids, a fact that the Holdens had not mentioned. It was also remembered by the kennel staff that "Biba" had suddenly developed a passion for chicken mince when previously she wouldn't touch it.

On the third day of the hearing, in an unprecedented move after the jury had been asked to leave the court, Recorder Thomas Field-Fisher Q.C., who is joint chairman of the R.S.P.C.A.'s legal advisory committee, signed a special order, involving an operation on Biba to find out whether she had been spayed. This was carried out under a general anaesthetic by Mr Michael Findlay described by the prosecution as the greatest cat expert in the country. Later he said he was satisfied that Biba had been effectively spayed.

When Dr Holden gave evidence on September 28th he said that neither of the cats was his. The jury decided otherwise and were satisfied that Biba's identity had been established beyond reasonable doubt. Sentencing Dr Holden, Recorder Thomas Field-Fisher told him "your value as a doctor is more outside than in prison". It was astonishing, he said, that the doctor could behave in such a way in carrying out the offence and that he was prepared to blame everyone except himself.

Hampsire County Council had been paying £56 a month to keep both cats in quarantine for the fifteen months it took to bring the case to court. The £1,000 costs awarded against Dr Holden would go towards this and the Council's legal expenses.

As far as is known the case is unique but as the prosecuting Q.C. said "There's no doubt at all that Dr Holden would have got clean away with it but for a very bad piece of luck for him". It is known that animal owners visiting their pets in quarantine are free to bring in what they like and are left alone with their animals during their visits. Is there then, not a case for the onus of ensuring that no other animals are brought in or taken out of quarantine establishments, being placed on their proprietors. It might also assist in any future, similar case as Dr Holden's if all animals were photographed on arrival in quarantine so that identity could be more easily established.

# ACKNOWLEDGEMENTS

I should like to thank the following for allowing me to use the material from their publications :—

The Office of Health Economics — Rabies.
The British Small Animal Veterinary Association — Report of their Working Party.
The Surrey Constabulary — Report on the Camberley Incident.
The World Health Organisation — Report of Expert Committee on Rabies—Sixth Report.
Michael Gaisford —— *Farmers Weekly*—— Port Watch as Rabies Nears the Channel.
City of London—Public Relations Department—Booklet on New Animal Quarantine Station at Heathrow.
*District Council Review ·*
H.M. Stationery Office — Report on the Committee of Inquiry on Rabies Final Report.

My grateful thanks are also due to the *Sussex Express and County Herald.*
Mr C. G. Caswell, the World Health Organisation.
H.M. Stationery Office.
The Animal Welfare Trust.
The Office of Health Economics.
The East Sussex County Council and the Surrey Constabulary for help in providing and giving permission to use photographs and illustrations.

*142*

# BIBLIOGRAPHY

*Re Chapter 1*
Agriculture Ministry of    *Final Report of the Committee of Inquiry into Rabies*
June 1971 "Chapter 2"

*Daily Mail*    *Rabies and The Dangers We all Face*    June 1976

Rhodes Richard    *"The Boy Who Conquered Rabies" Readers Digest*
Condensed from Redbrook 1971 published by the McCall Publishing Company 1971

Thompson Glyn D    "Rabies" *Environmental Health* August 1976

Turner Dr G. S.    Virologist, Lister Institute of Preventive Medicine, *Paper to Zoology Section 1976*

*Re Chapter 2*
Agriculture Ministry of    *Final Report of the Committee of Inquiry into Rabies*
June 1971 "Chapter 4"

Thompson Glyn D    "Rabies" *Environmental Health* August 1976

West Geoffrey P    *Rabies in Animals and Man* "Chapter 3" published by David and Charles, Newton Abbott

*Re Chapter 3*

Surrey Constabulary     *Report on Rabies at Camberley, 1970*

*Re Chapter 4*

Agriculture Ministry of .*Final Report of the Committee of Inquiry into Rabies*
June 1971 "Chapter 6"

Gibbs Roy     *Rural District Review* "Dread dog Disease Reappears" June 1970

*City of London Public Relations Department.*
"Booklet on Heathrow Animal Quarantine Station."

*Re Chapter 5*

Agriculture Ministry of *Final Report of the Committee of Inquiry into Rabies*
June 1971 "Chapter 2"

Office of Health Economics     *Rabies* 1976

West Geoffrey P     *Rabies in Animals and Man* "Chapter 2" published by David and Charles, Newton Abbott

*Re Chapter 6*

Agriculture Ministry of *Memorandum on Rabies* Appendix 1, July 1976

**Bland Clifford**     *Personal experience of anti-rabies vaccination* Interview with author, 1976

**Office of Health Economics**     *Rabies* 1976

## Bibliography

West Geoffrey P.      *Rabies in Animals and Man* *"Chapter 7"*

World Health Organisation      *Expert Committee on Rabies, Sixth Report* 1973

*Re Chapter 7*

Agriculture Ministry of *Letter to airline operators re crating of animals* August 1975

Agriculture Ministry of *Letter to shipping and airline operators re boarding documents* September 1974

H.M. Stationery Office *Rabies [Importation of Dogs, Cats and Other Mammals] Order, 1974*

*Re Chapter 8*

Daily Mail      *"Dog lovers took a deadly gamble"* — *"Dog smuggled in at Whitstable"* January 14th 1976

Daily Mail      *"Boxer dog "Simba" smuggled in at Dover"* 1976

Daily Telegraph      *"Couple jailed for smuggling two dogs"* 1976

Daily Telegraph      *"Mexican woman who hid dog, find £650,00" 1976*

Daily Telegraph      *"Pet smugglers jailed for four months"* 1976

Gibb M. R.                    *District Coucil Review.*
                              ''Problems of a Stowaway Cat.''

                              *District Council Review''.*
                              ''Rabies publicity on Dog Licence
                              Reminders.''

*Re Chapter 9*
Animal Welfare Trust     *''Pamphlet — A smuggled Dog can
                         kill a child* Published by McKay
                         Chatham

*Re Chapter 10*
Agriculture Ministry of  *Final Report of Committee of
                         Inquiry into Rabies* ''Disease
                         control Measures in Europe''
                         Chapter 9

West Geoffrey P          *Rabies in Animals and Man*
                         ''Chapter 6'' published by David
                         and Charles, Newton Abbott

World Health             *Expert Committee on Rabies Sixth
   Organisation          Report* 1973 ''Control of rabies in
                         domesticated animals'' ''Chapter
                         11''

*Re Chapter 11*
H.M. Stationery Office   *Rabies Control Order 1974*

Rabies Control Plan      *Report by County Estates Sur-
                         veyor, East Sussex County Counci'*
                         March 1976

## Bibliography

*Re Chapter 12*
British Small Animal   *Report of Rabies Working Party*
  Veterinary Association 1976

*Re Chapter 13*
Agriculture Ministry of   *The Rabies [Importation of Dogs, Cats and Other Mammals] Order 1974*
        Notes for Guidance''

Thomas Terry   *District Council Review April 1977.* ''Something to Bark About in Afan''

British Small Animal   *Report of Rabies Working Party 1976*
  Veterinary Association

        *Dogs — Report of the Interdepartmental Enquiry* On August 1976

World Health   *Expert Committe on Rabies Sixth Report* 1973 ''Treatment of Confirmed Rabies in Man Chapter 11''
  Organisation

# INDEX

# *Index*

*149*

# Rabies—You and Your Pets

Russia 60
Rabies (Control Order) 1974 73, 105
 111
Roskill, Lord 80
Rocq, Henri 130
S
South America 9
Southern Command 34
Surrey Constabulary 37
Second World War 52
Saxony 13
Switzerland 13, 27, 63
Sweden 13, 39
Spain 27, 88
Semple 58
South Africa 76, 134
Surrey Heath D.C. 96
San Quentin Prison 124
Sikes Dr. R.K. 137
Smyth John Q.C. 140
T
Turner Dr. G.S. 17
Tomlin, Stan 83

"The Rabid Summer" 89
Thomas, Terry 120
Turkey 134
Trinidad 137
U
U.S. Department of Health 26
U.S.A. 50, 52, 60, 102, 135
Ulster S.P.C.A. 126
W
Winkler, Matt 18
World Health Organisation 24, 38, 58
 61, 98, 102, 117, 134
Waterhouse Committee 38, 42, 50,
 62, 63, 64
Wye 28
Weekly Epidemiological Record 104
West Midlands County Council 110
Wilson, Harold 118
Winchester Crown Court 139
Y
Yugoslavia 17, 135
Z
Zaire 82

## 250 YEARS AFTER SIR CHRISTOPHER WREN
### A. D. COBBAN

The Stuart Period in which Wren lived was eventful and saw the fall of Charles I and the Civil War, England ruled by a Lord Protector and the eventual Restoration.

During this time the art and science of building flourished under Wren the master. He was forty years of age before turning his talent to architecture and he was to spend the next fifty years designing and building. He was versatile and prolific as can be seen from his many designs.

This book is intended to highlight some of Wren's work of which St. Paul's, fifty-four of the City churches, and other secular buildings, remain as examples of his extraordinary talents.

ISBN 0 85475 089 4                                          Illustrated.


## BLIGHTY

To soldiers in the trenches in 1914-18 Blighty seemed a comparative Paradise. But what was life in England really like in those momentous years? Many books have described the rigours and horrors of life at the battle fronts during those years but few have described life for the civilian keeping the home fires burning.

In this book we see the life of ordinary Britons during this shattering time. We see them adjusting to the bewildering changed conditions of life, wrestling with their problems in industrial and domestic life, and generally seeing it through. This in spite of the all too often loss of a near and dear one.

The young and middle-aged will find much to intrigue and enlighten them, while the over 60's with their own personal memories of those stirring times will find even more.

ISBN 0 85475 114 9                                          Illustrated.

*Published by*
    VENTON EDUCATIONAL LTD., The Uffington Press,
      High Street, MELKSHAM, Wiltshire, SN12 6LA

# Rare and Exciting Cars

DAPHNE BAMPTON

The biographies of 26 rare motor-cars are described in this book; cars that were young in the dawn of the motoring era and in the stately Edwardian age; cars from the 1920's — a great period in the development of motor transport — and vehicles of a more recent time. There are cars that have spent 40 or 50 years decaying in old sheds before being found and restored to their former elegance in a world that their original owners could never have imagined, and there are mighty racers from the days of Brooklands.

These are the vehicles whose biographies Daphne Bampton records with vivid detail. She relates the history of an exciting "horseless carriage" from the 1890's, and the disastrous adventures of a Vauxhall 30/98 in the Australian bush. The first car on Gozo is portrayed, and a Grand Prix Alfa Romeo that bears the legendary Scuderia Ferrari motif on its bonnet. There is the history of a perky cyclecar that still runs on wire and bobbin steering and of the Rolls - Royce Silver Ghost that once belonged to a great American Lady.

Brief engine specifications are given, but it is the social history of each vehicle that predominates, because this is a book for the general reader — a book for those who like cars, people and history, since all three are woven together in these pages.

ISBN 0 85475 118 1  *Illustrated.*

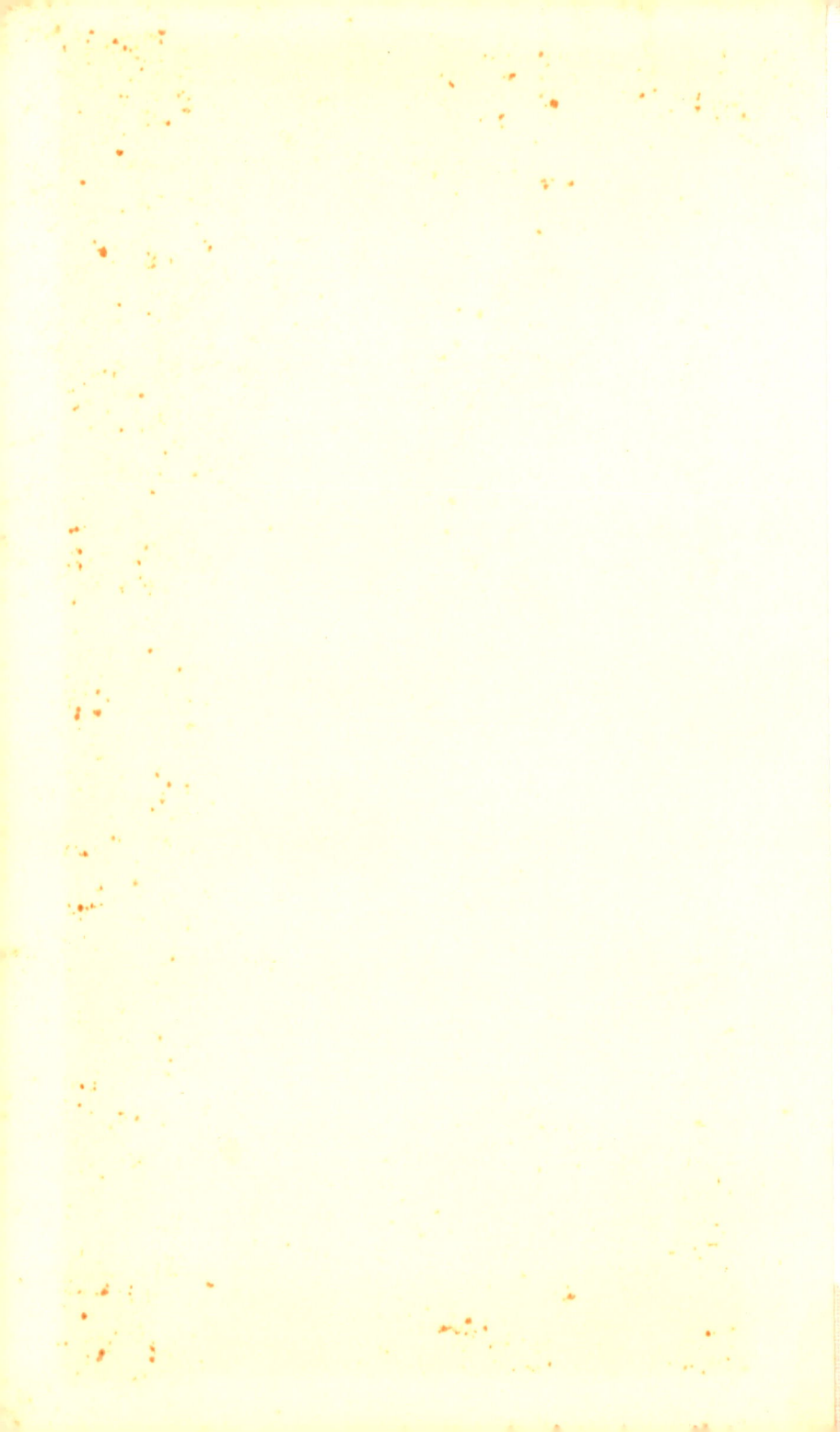